Contents — Cello Book Two

GW00643934

Boil 'em cabbage down

Trad. American

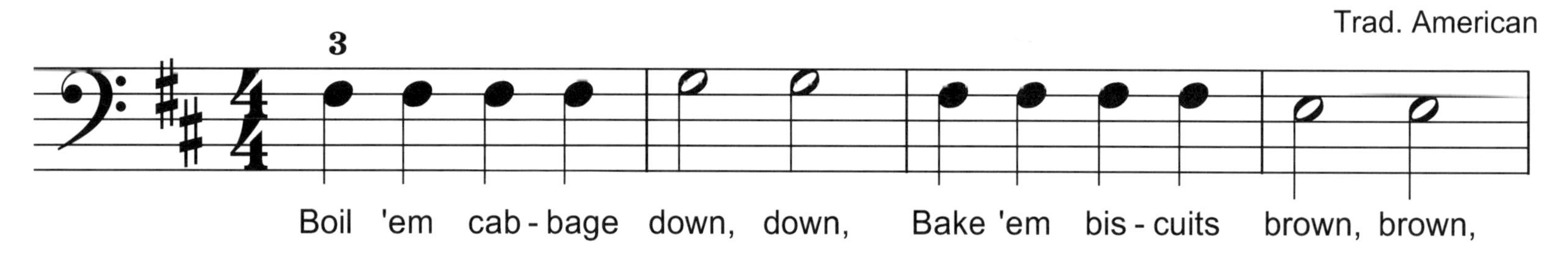
3
Boil 'em cab - bage down, down, Bake 'em bis - cuits brown, brown,

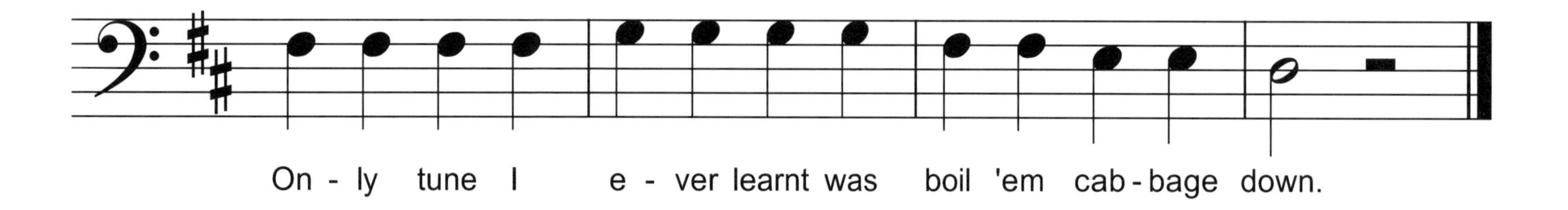
On - ly tune I e - ver learnt was boil 'em cab - bage down.

11-9-17

pizz + bowed

Happy days

Slavonic folk song

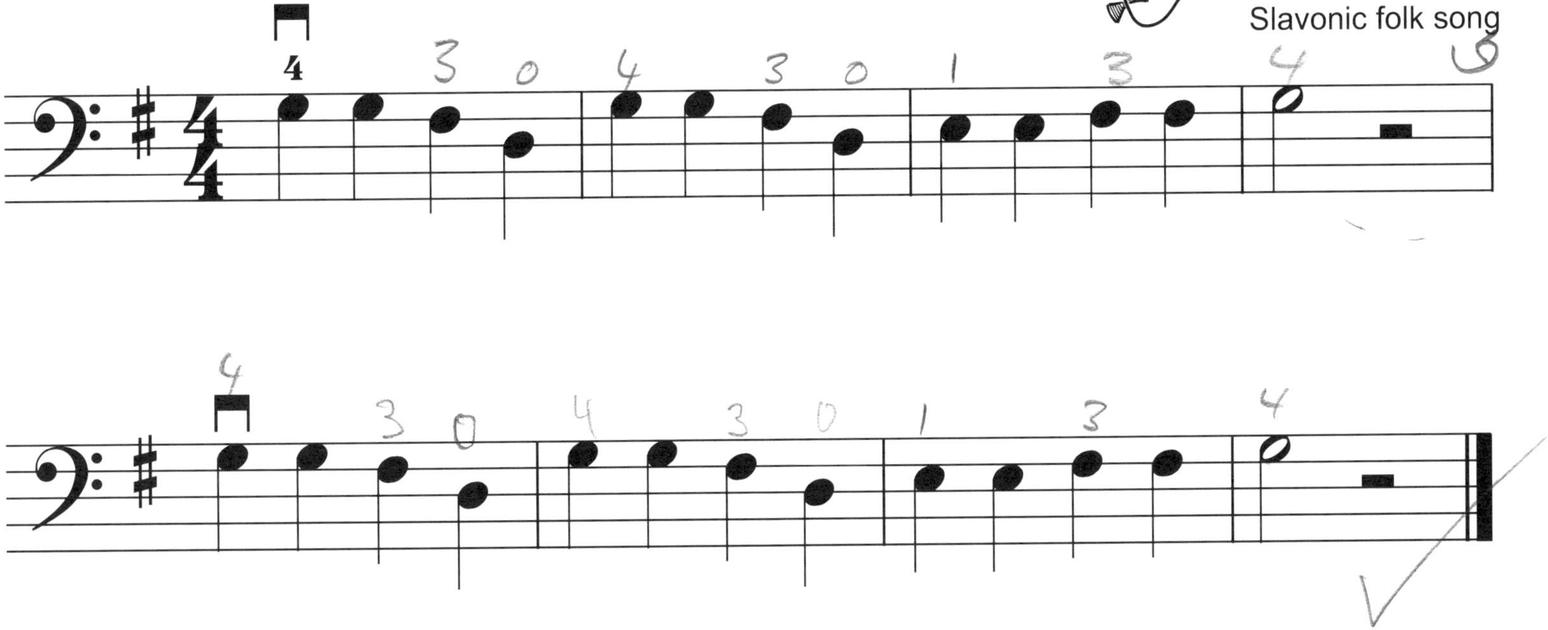

Now the day is over

S. Baring-Gould
(1834-1924)

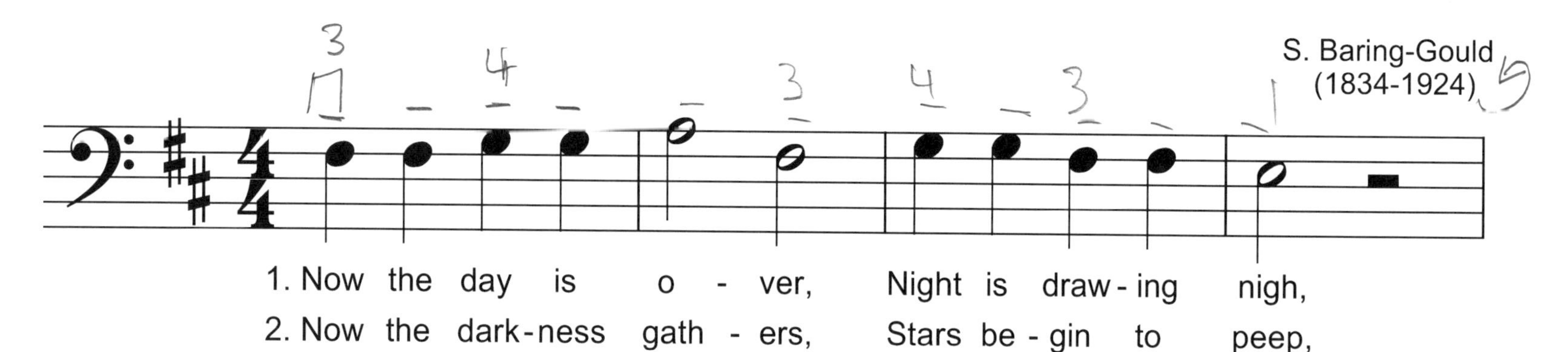
1. Now the day is o - ver, Night is draw - ing nigh,
2. Now the dark - ness gath - ers, Stars be - gin to peep,

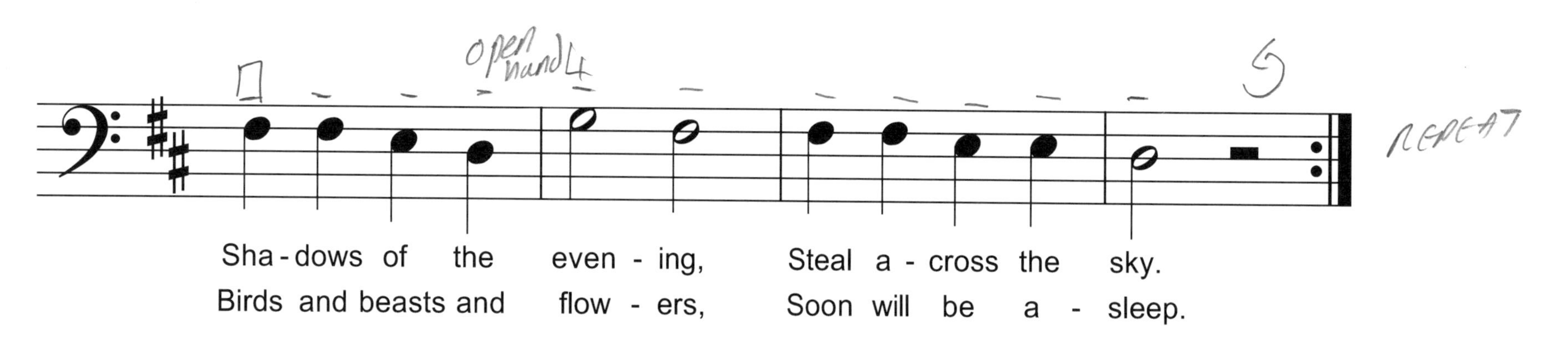
Sha - dows of the even - ing, Steal a - cross the sky.
Birds and beasts and flow - ers, Soon will be a - sleep.

Slurs join notes together in the same bow.

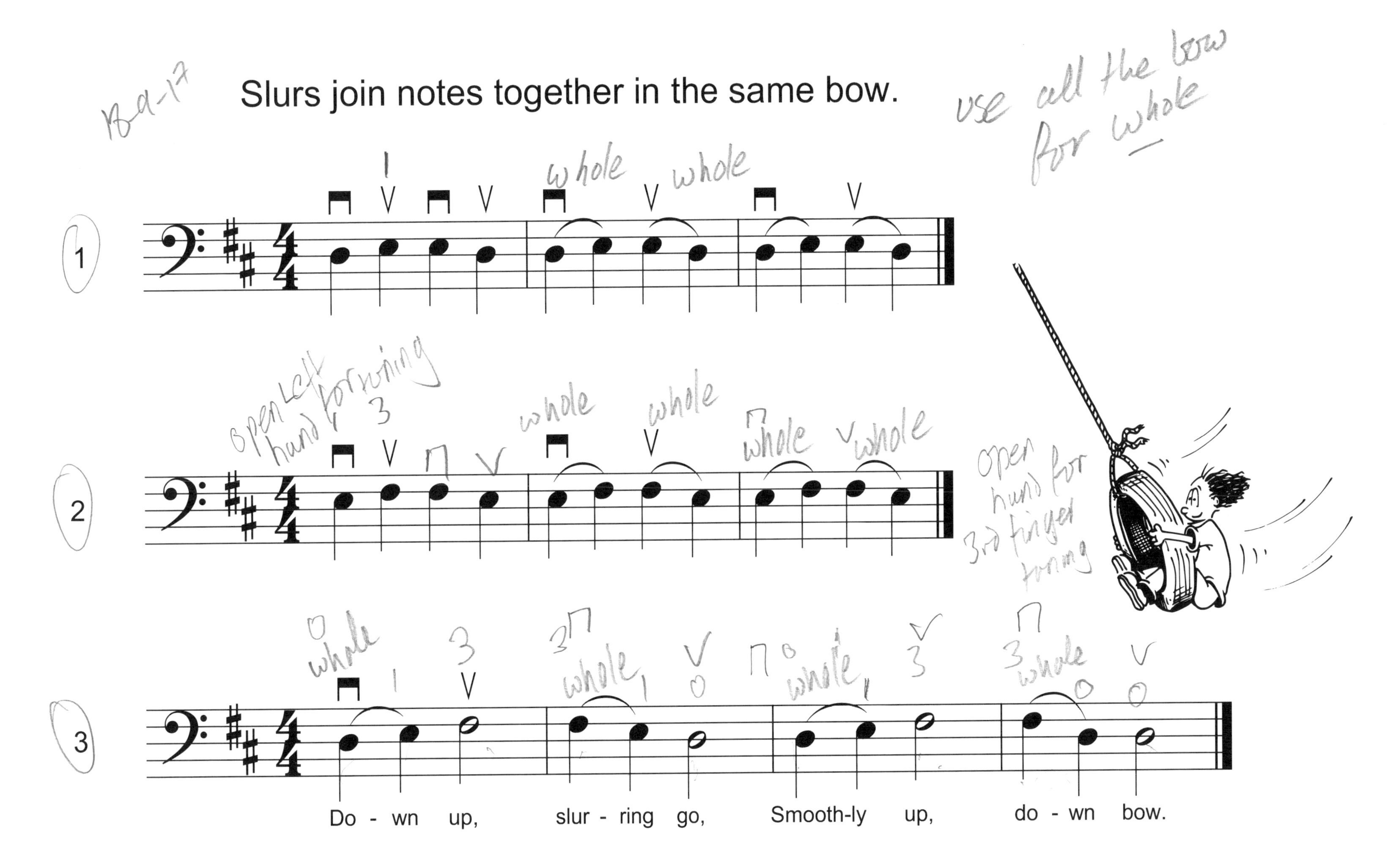
1
2
3
Do - wn up, slur - ring go, Smooth-ly up, do - wn bow.

Merry dance
16C French melody

Lucy Locket

Trad.

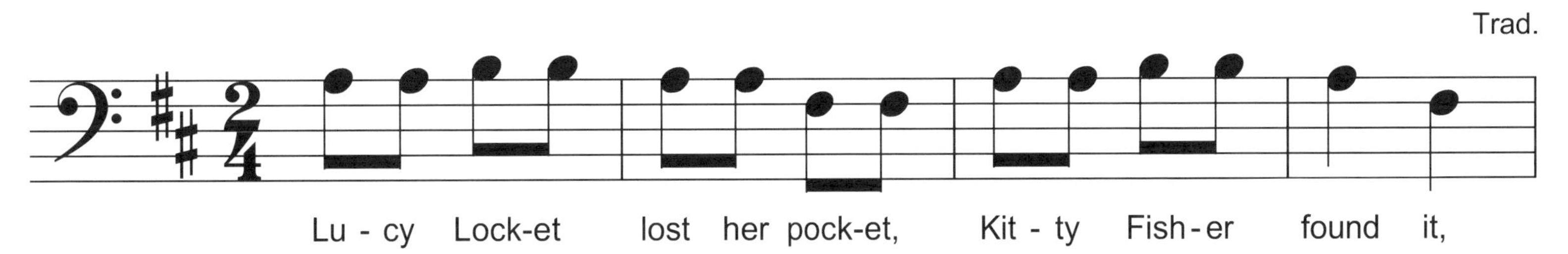
Lu - cy Lock-et lost her pock-et, Kit - ty Fish - er found it,

Not a pen - ny was there in it, on - ly rib - bon round it.

16-10-17

Bell song

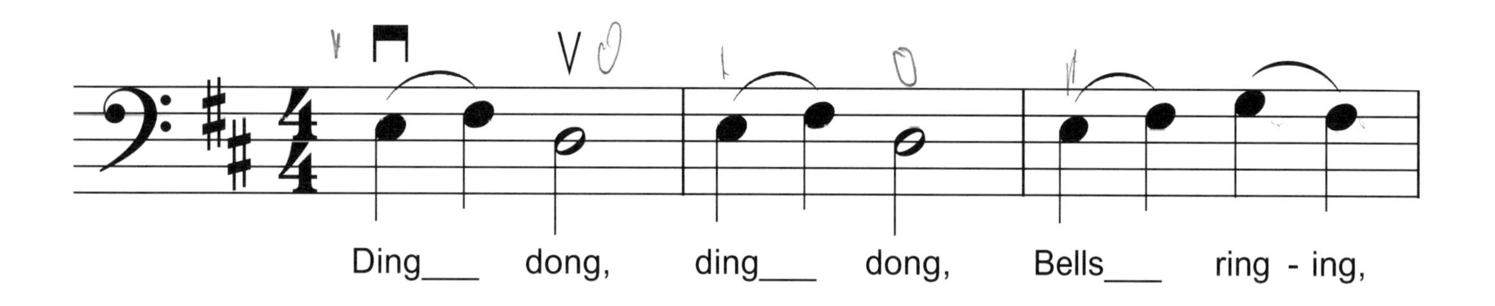
Ding___ dong, ding___ dong, Bells___ ring - ing,

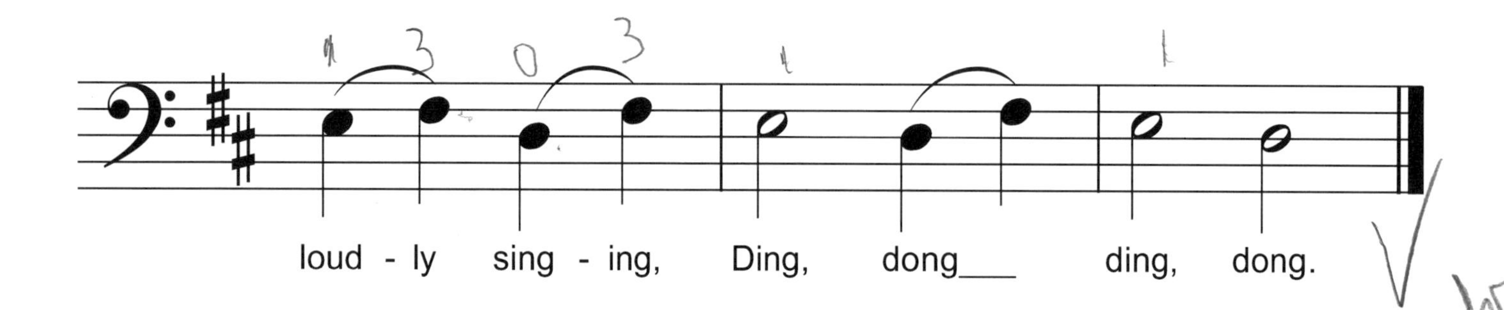
loud - ly sing - ing, Ding, dong___ ding, dong.

play for fun

Frère Jacques

Trad. round

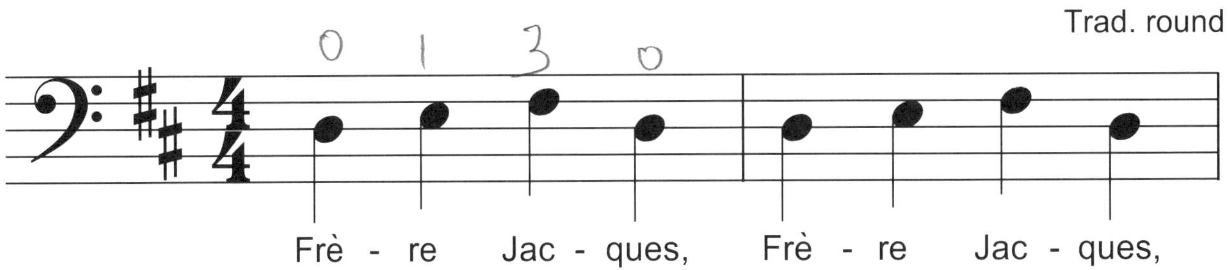
Frè - re Jac - ques, Frè - re Jac - ques,

"SNORE"
"SNORE"

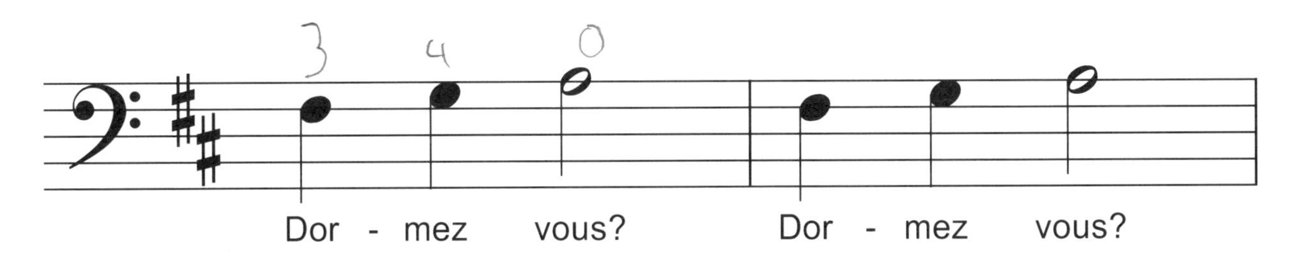
Dor - mez vous? Dor - mez vous?

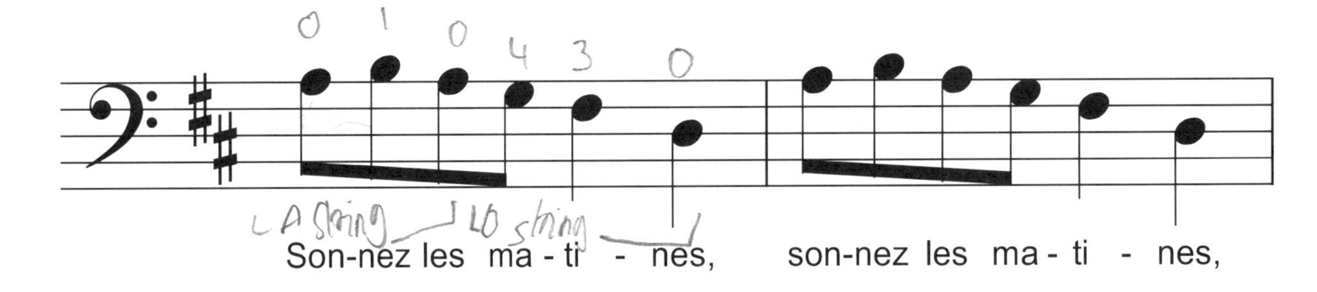
Son-nez les ma - ti - nes, son-nez les ma - ti - nes,

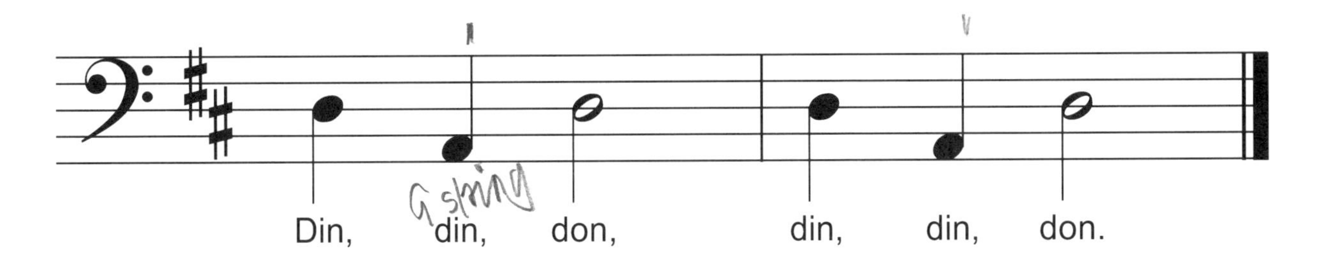
Din, din, don, din, din, don.

Frère Jacques

"DIN"
"DIN"
"DON"

Cobbler, cobbler

Trad.

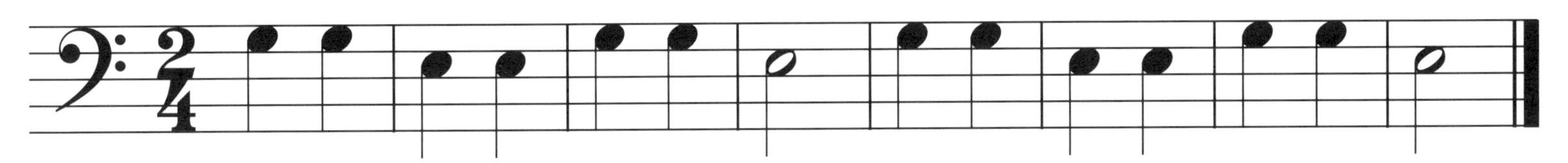
Cob - bler, cob - bler, mend my shoe, Have it done by half-past two.

Rain, rain, go away

Trad.
Rain, rain, go a - way. Come a - gain an - oth - er day.

Baa, baa, black sheep

Trad.

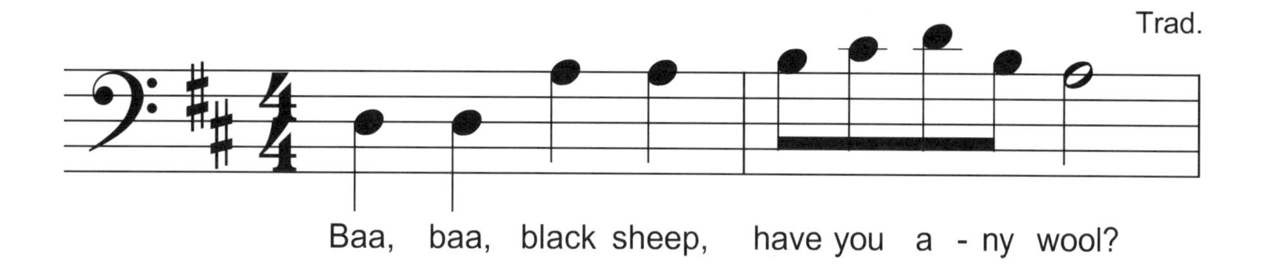
Baa, baa, black sheep, have you a - ny wool?

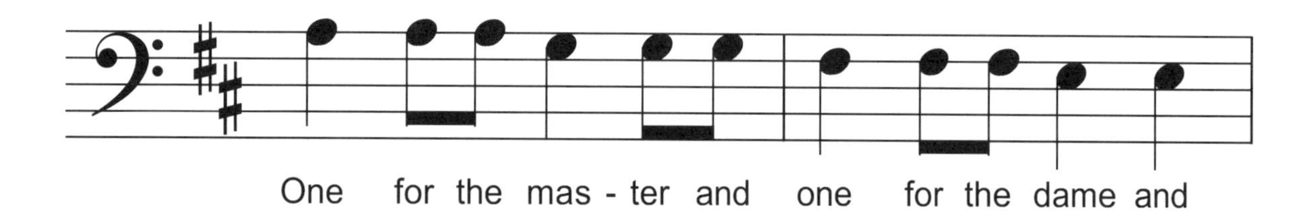
Yes sir, yes sir, three bags full.

LITTLE BOY

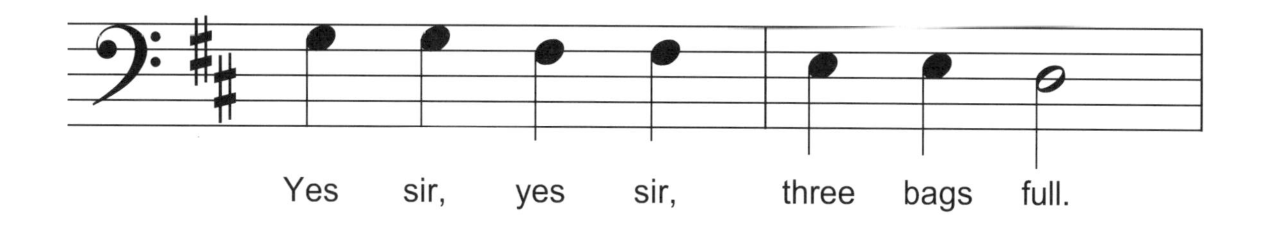
One for the mas - ter and one for the dame and

MASTER
DAME

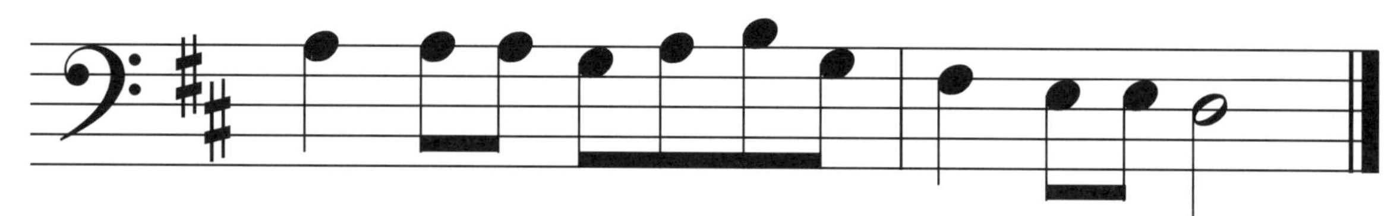
one for the lit - tle boy who lives down the lane.

Clock canon

Trad.

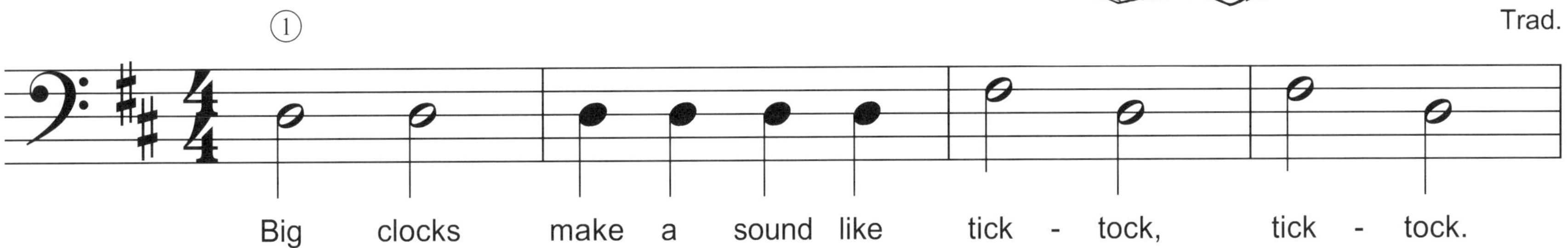
①
Big clocks make a sound like tick - tock, tick - tock.

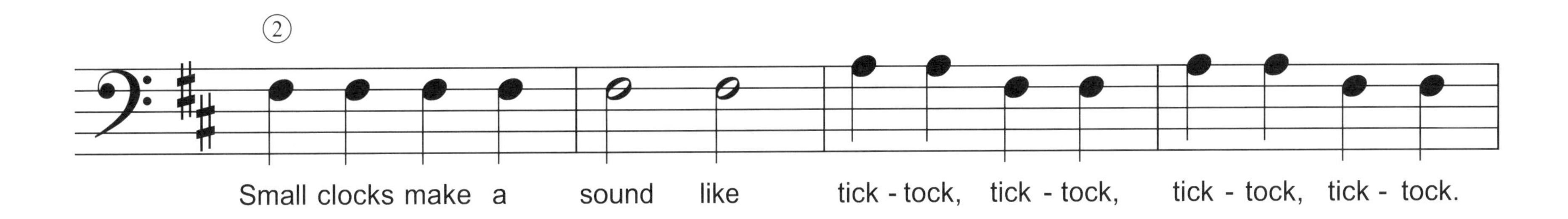
②
Small clocks make a sound like tick - tock, tick - tock, tick - tock, tick - tock.

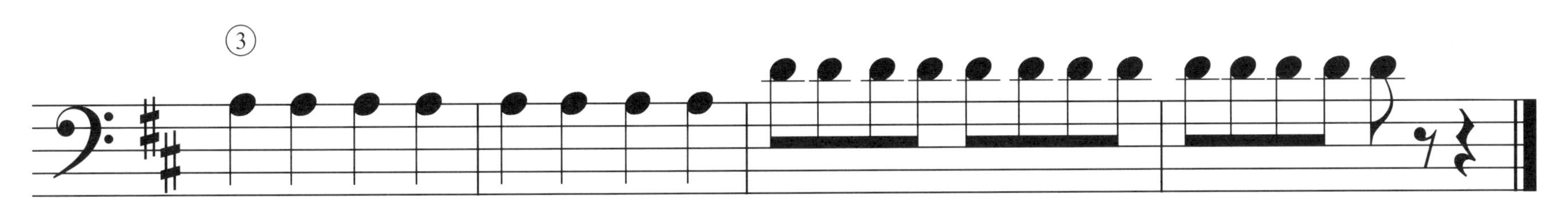
③
And the lit - tle ti - ny clocks go tick-a tock-a, tick-a tock-a, tick-a tock-a tick.

Dinah

Trad. American

No one in the house but Di - nah, Di - nah, No one in the house but me I know.

No one in the house but Di - nah, Di - nah, Play-ing on the old ban - jo.

Sailing on the ocean

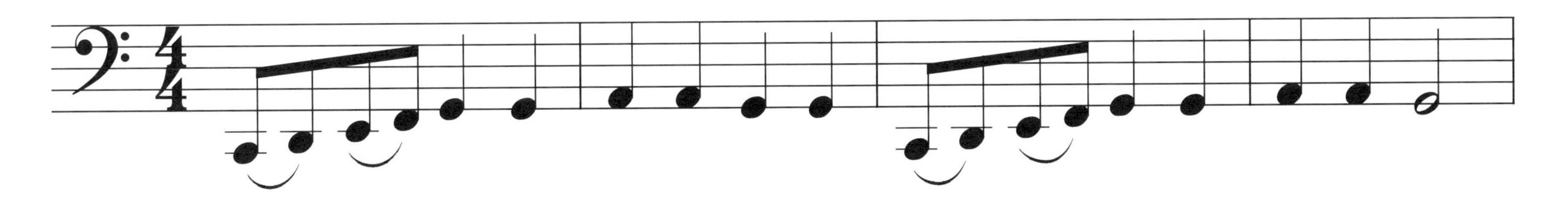

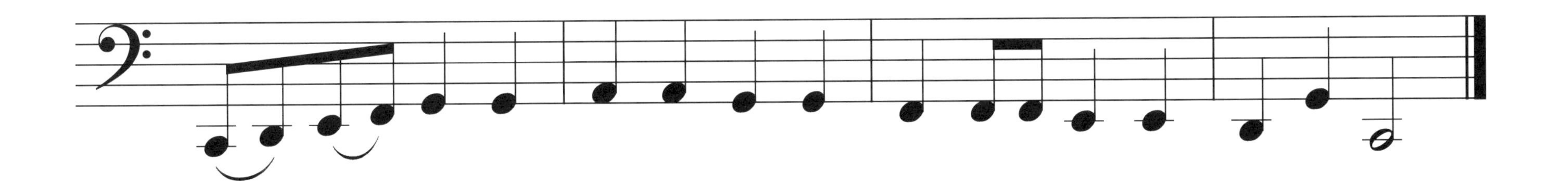

Crab crawling

Helen Blackman

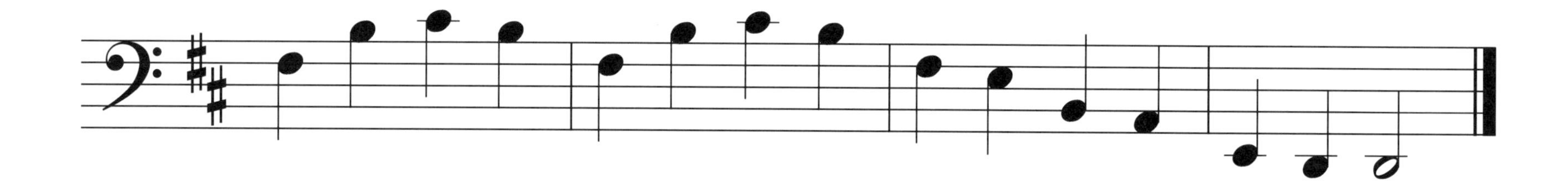

Folk dance

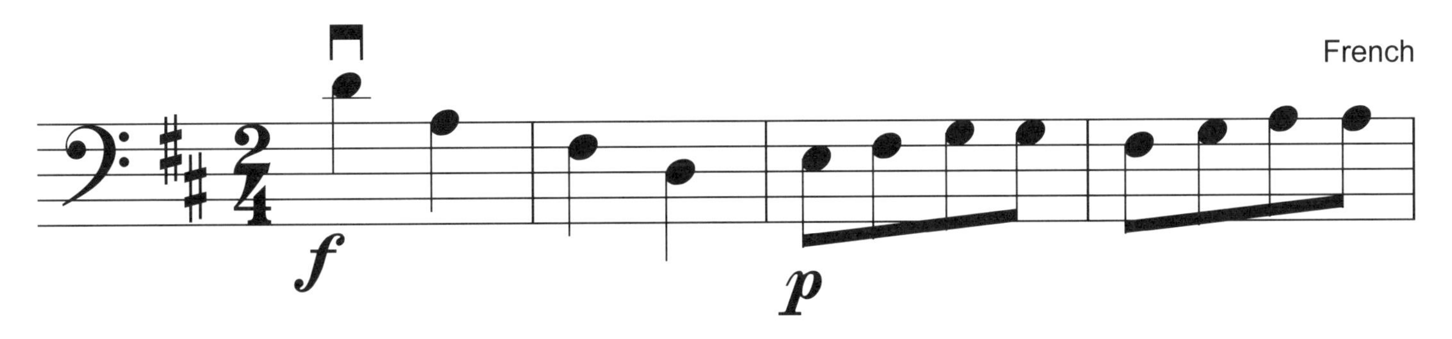
French
f
p

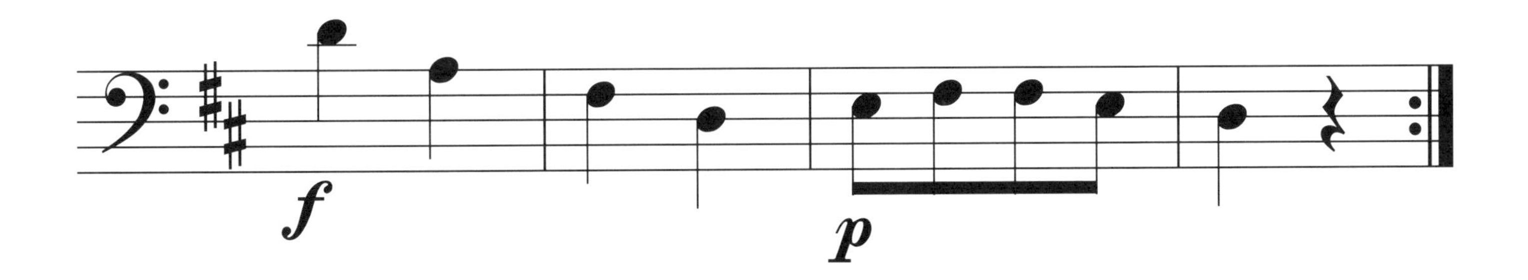
f
p

f (***forte***) = loudly ***p*** (***piano***) = softly

Evening song

17C French

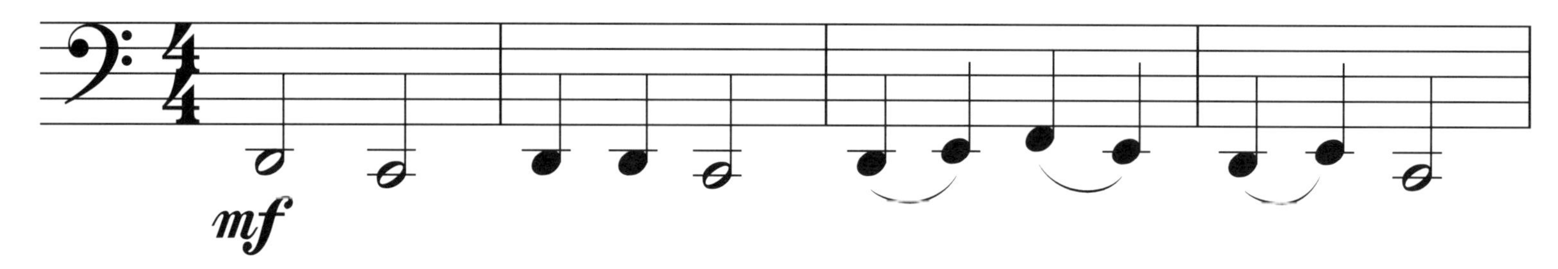
mf

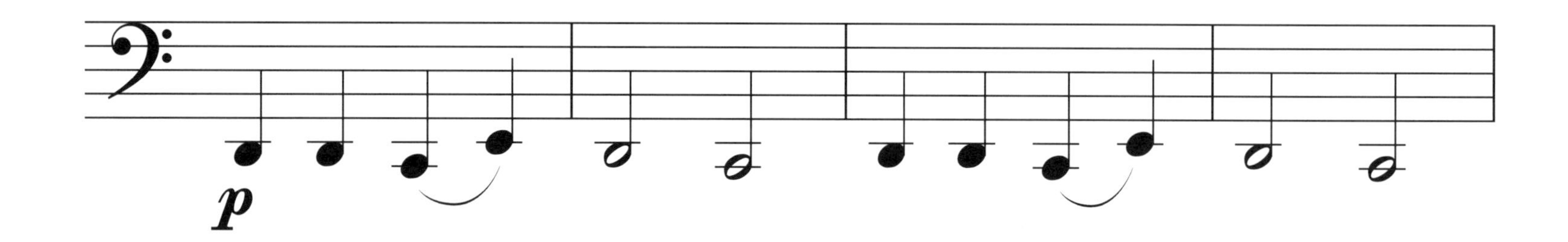
p

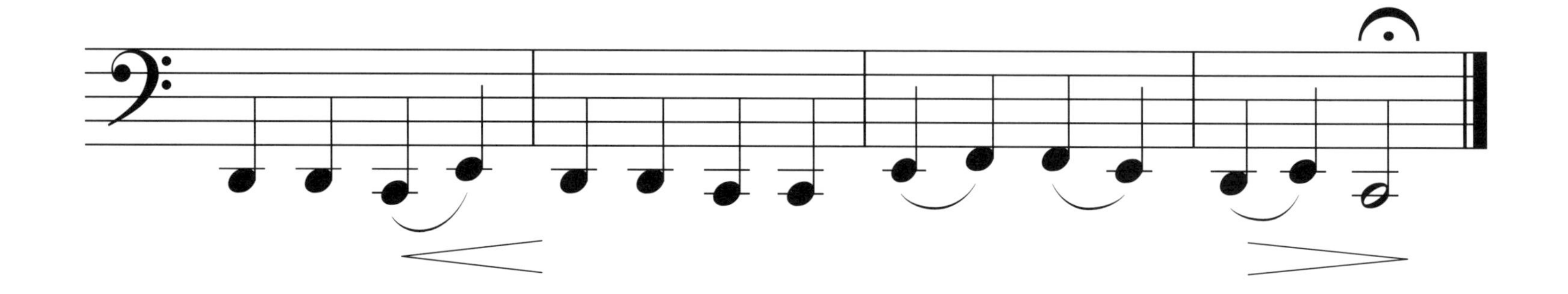

Listen!

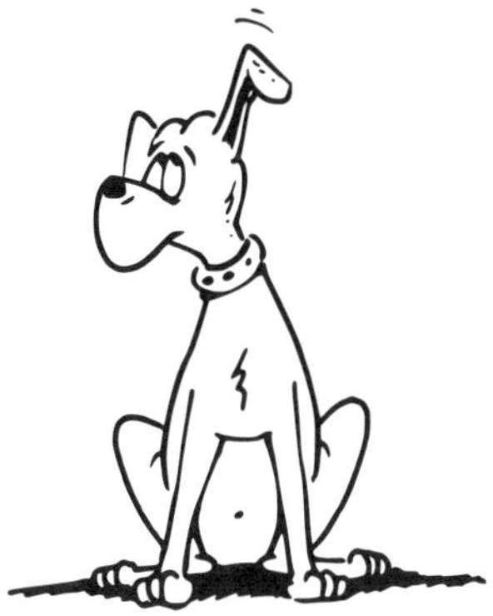

French

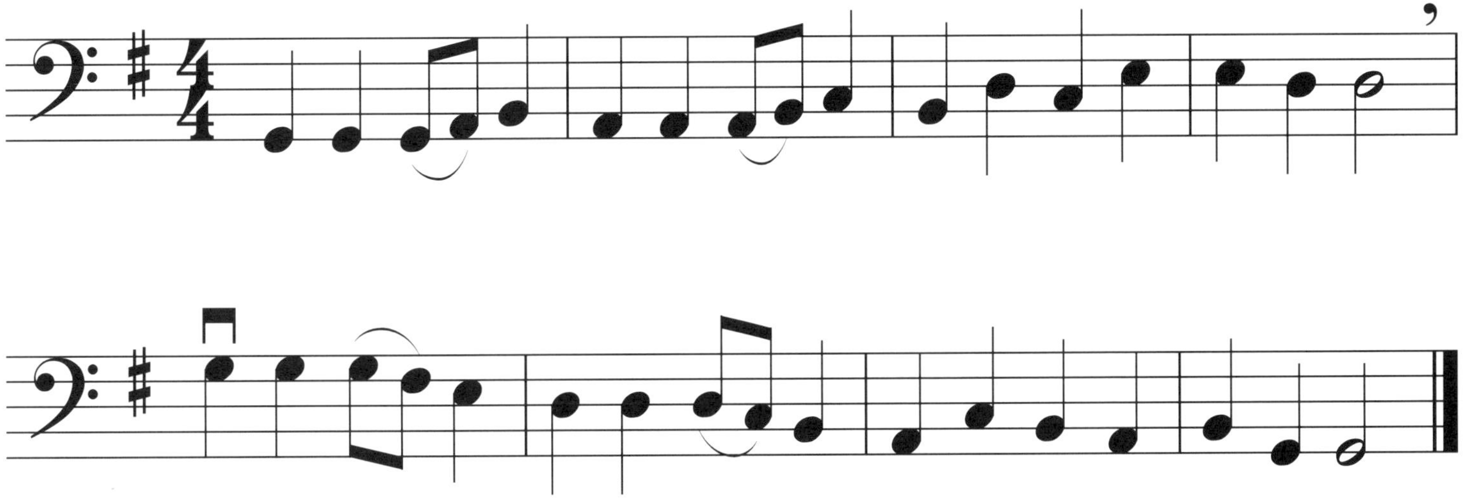

More crabs crawling

Helen Blackman

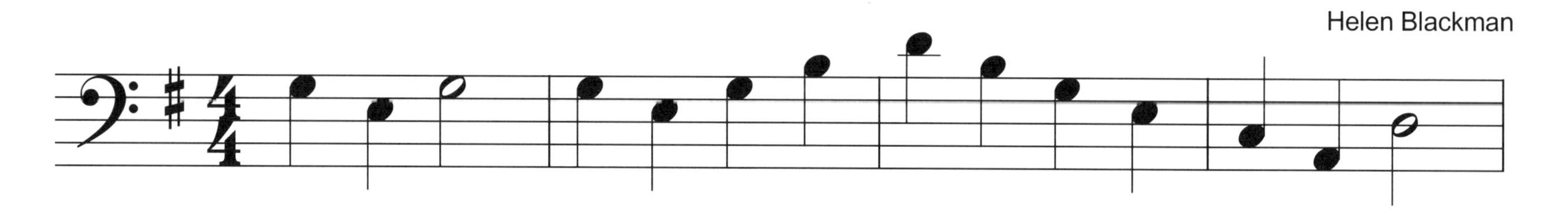

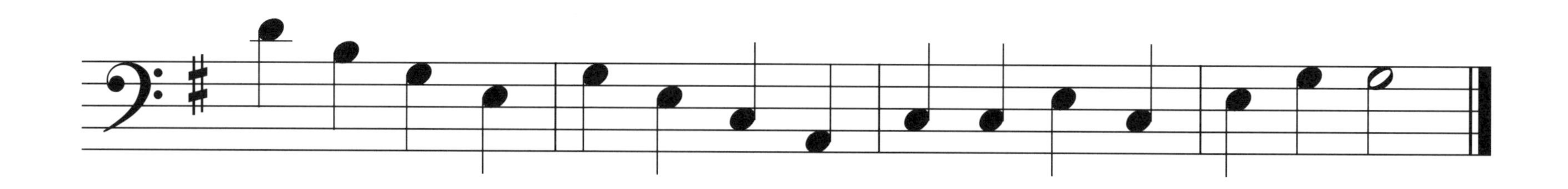

There is a happy land

Trad. Indian

Blue bells, cockle shells

Trad.

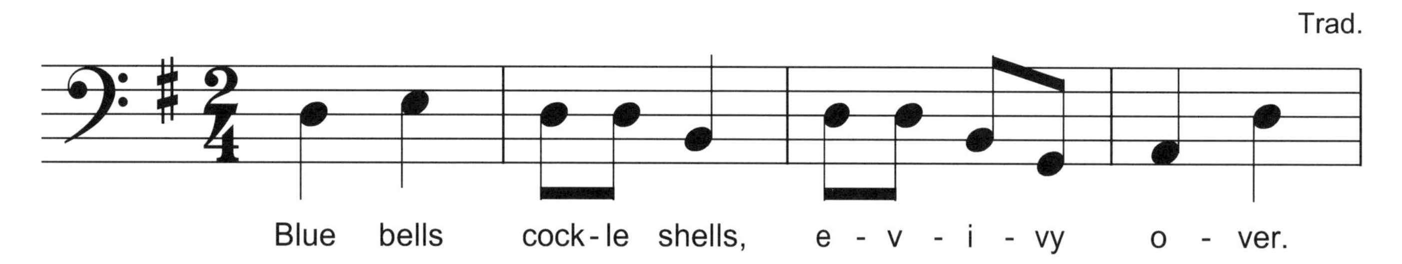
Blue bells cock - le shells, e - v - i - vy o - ver.

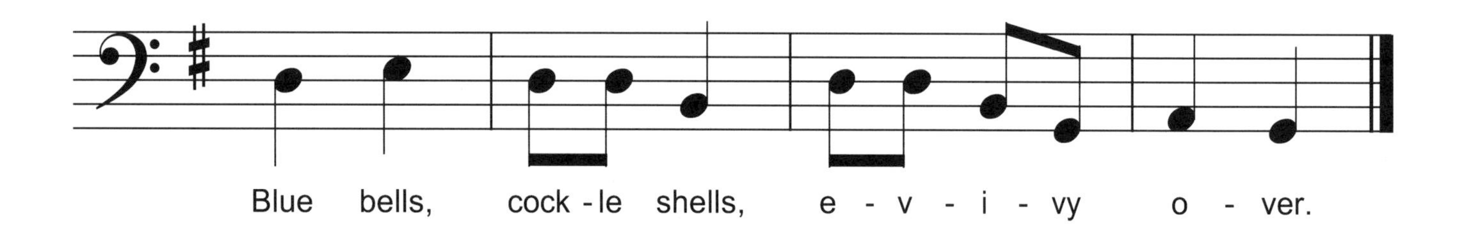
Blue bells, cock - le shells, e - v - i - vy o - ver.

This old man

Trad.

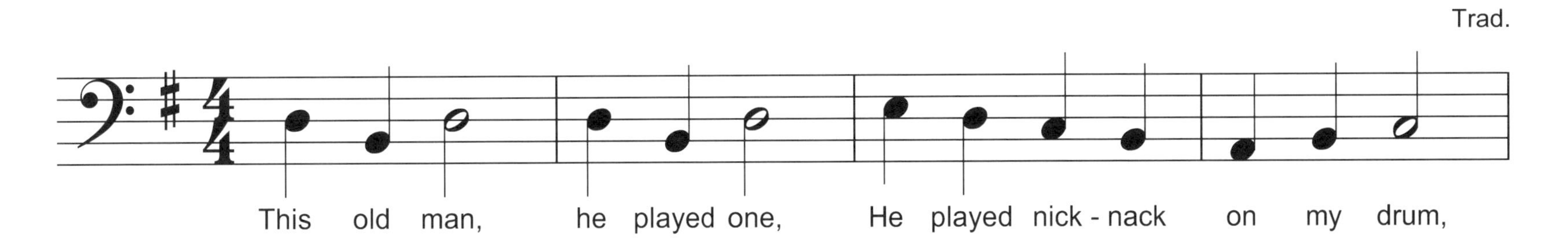
This old man, he played one, He played nick - nack on my drum,

Nick - nack, pad-dy whack, give a dog a bone, This old man came roll - ing home.

Feel the beat

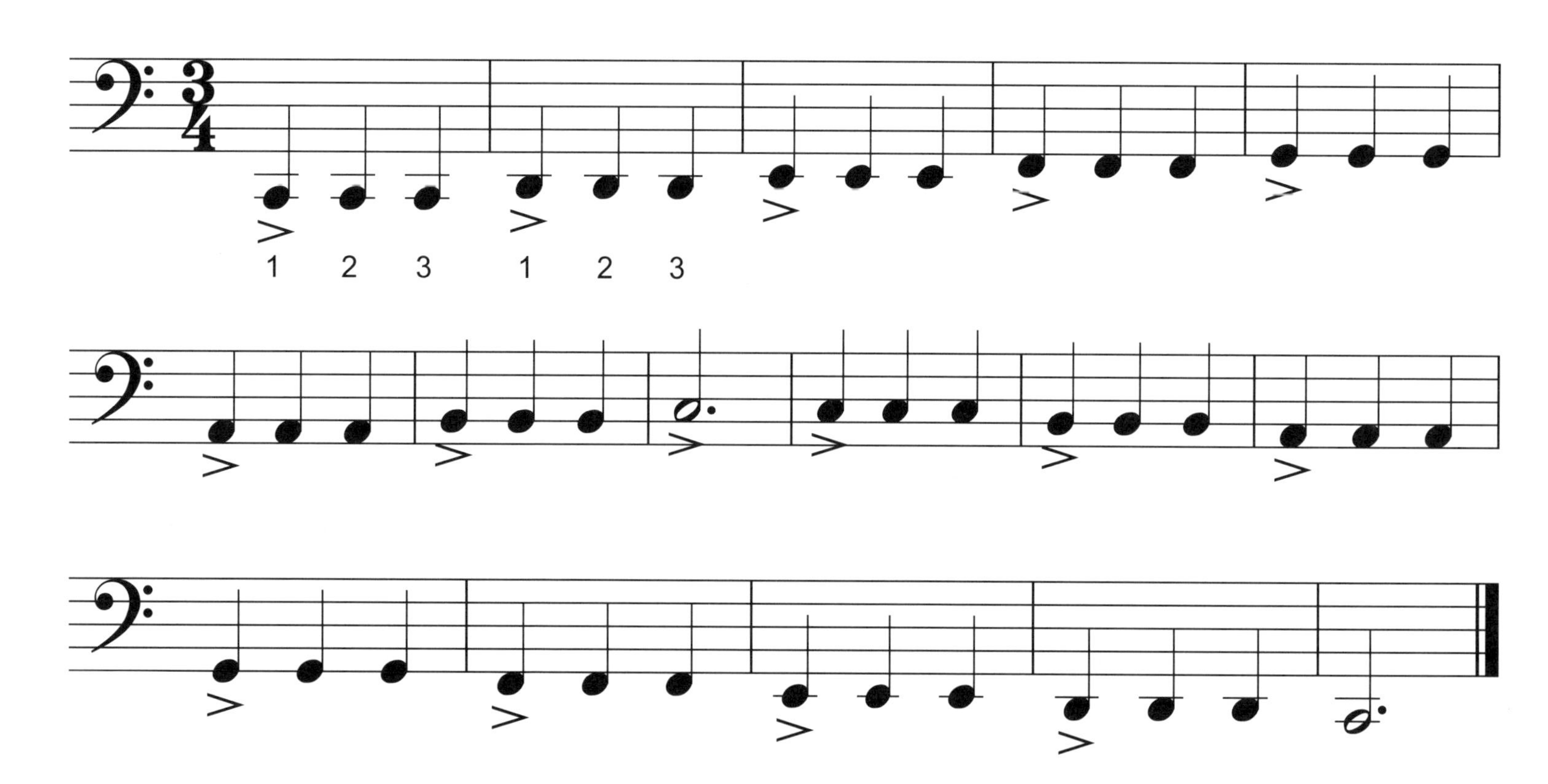
1 2 3 1 2 3

Two in the boat

Trad. American

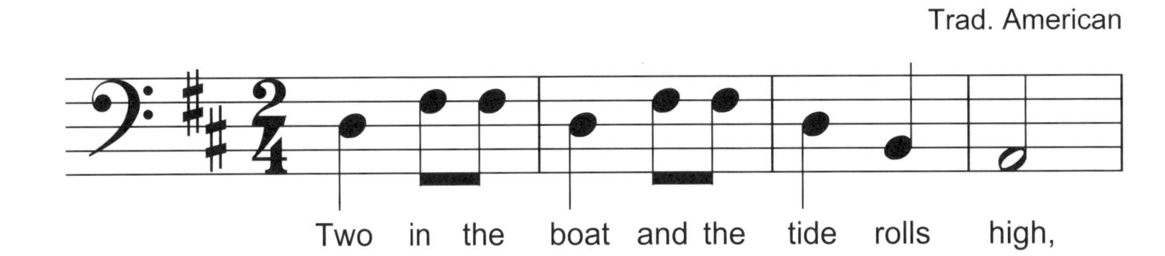
Two in the boat and the tide rolls high,

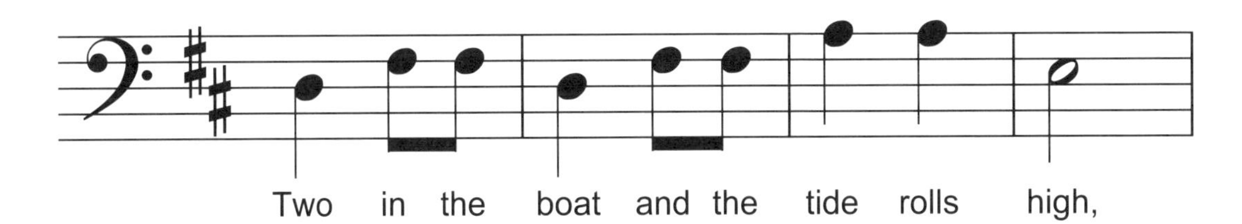
Two in the boat and the tide rolls high,

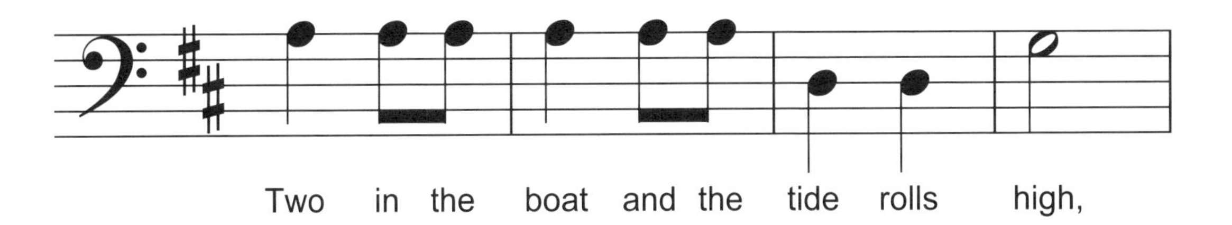
Two in the boat and the tide rolls high,

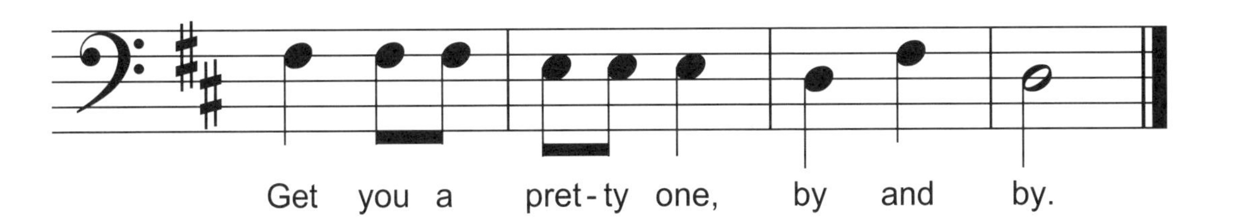
Get you a pret - ty one, by and by.

Bell horses

Trad.

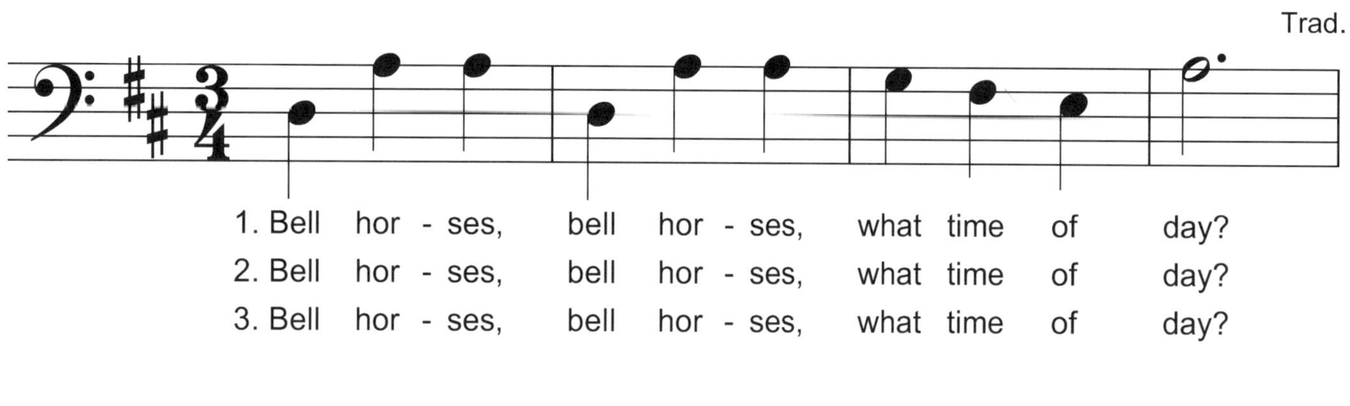

1. Bell hor - ses, bell hor - ses, what time of day?
2. Bell hor - ses, bell hor - ses, what time of day?
3. Bell hor - ses, bell hor - ses, what time of day?

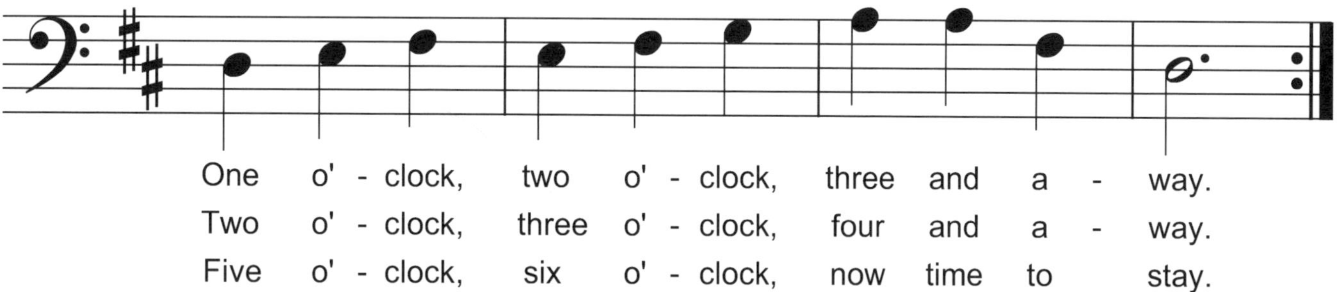

One o' - clock, two o' - clock, three and a - way.
Two o' - clock, three o' - clock, four and a - way.
Five o' - clock, six o' - clock, now time to stay.

French folk song

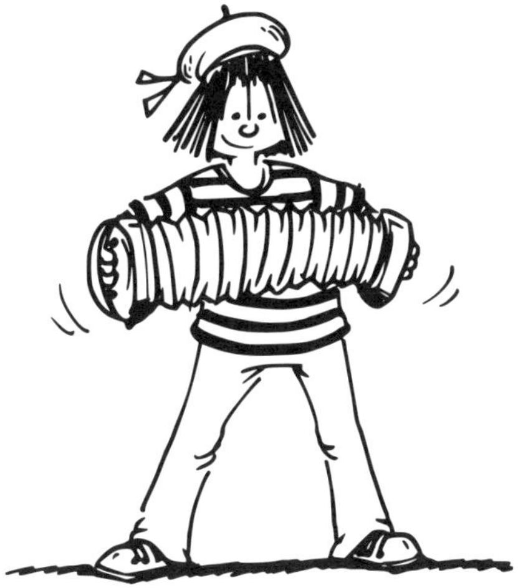

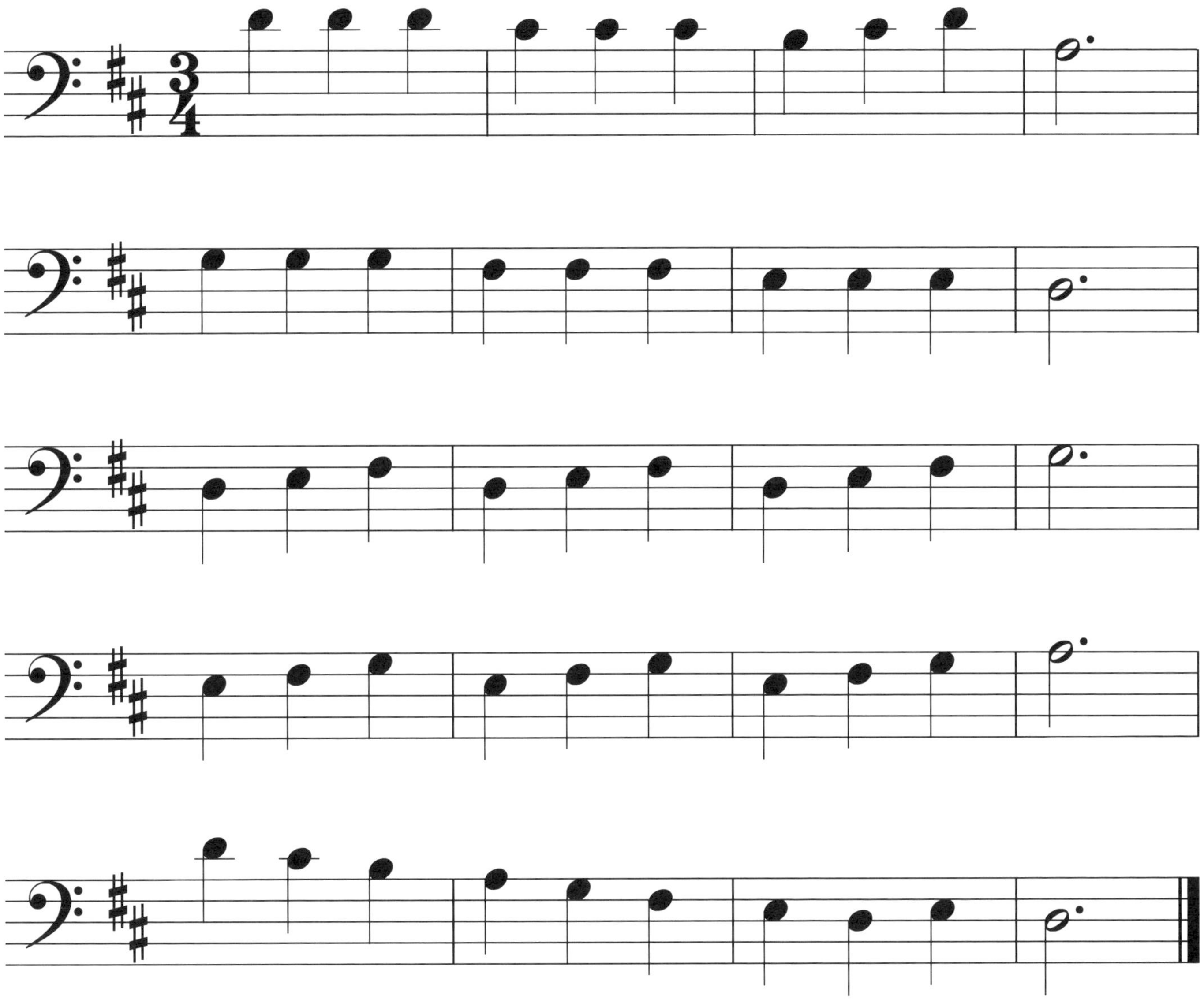

See saw sacradown

Trad. English
LONDON TOWN
See saw, sac - ra - down, Which is the
way to Lon - don Town? One foot up and one foot
down; That is the way to Lon - don Town.

Polka

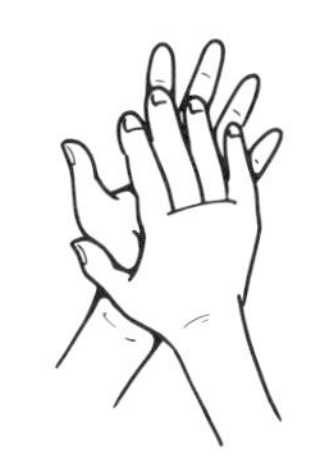

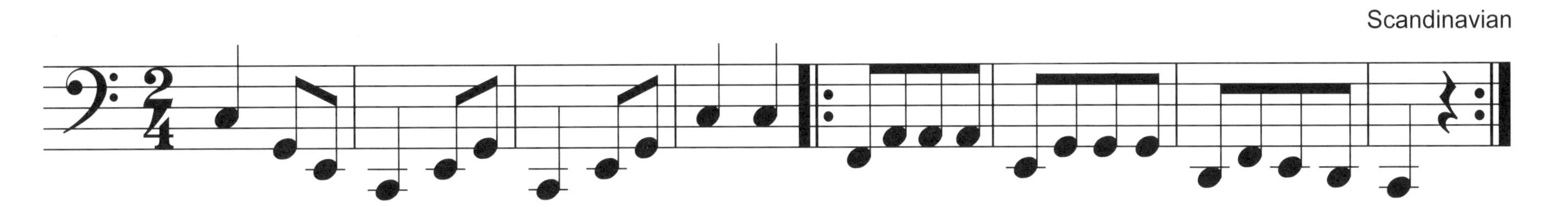
Scandinavian

My goose

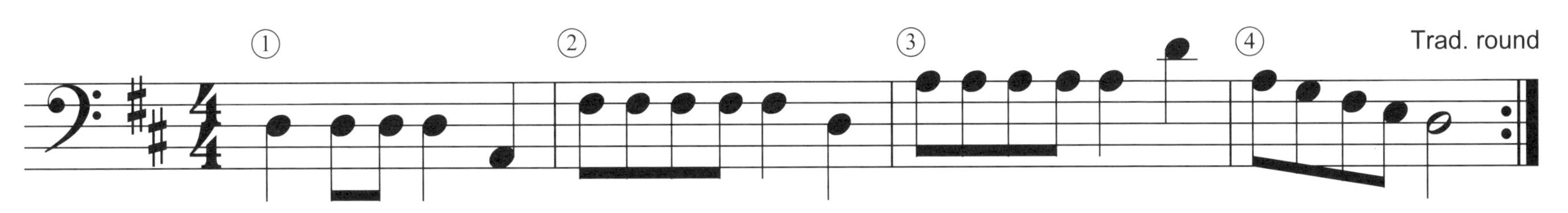
Trad. round
1
2
3
4
Why shouldn't my goose, Sing as well as thy goose, When I paid for my goose, Twice as much as thou.

Taffy was a Welshman

Trad.

Taf- fy was a Welshman Taf-fy was a thief. Taf-fy came to my house and stole a leg of beef.

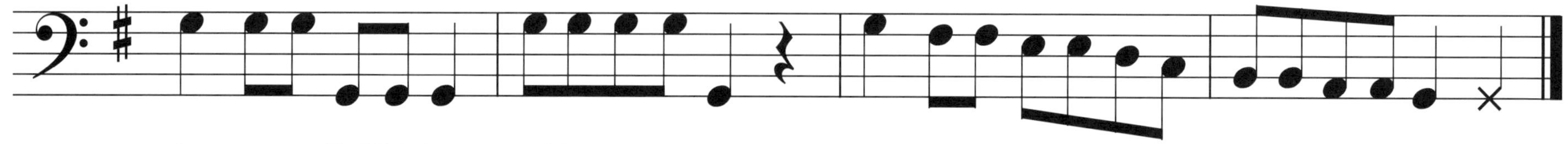

I came to Taf-fy's house, Taf-fy was in bed. I took a marrow bone and hit him on the head! Biff!

Lightly row
Trad.
Light - ly row, light - ly row, o'er the glas - sy waves we go;
Smooth-ly glide, smooth-ly glide, on the si - lent tide.
Let the winds and wa - ters be min - gled with our mel - o - dy;
Sing and float, sing and float, in our lit - tle boat.

Jingle bells

J. Pierpont

Jin - gle bells, jin - gle bells, jin - gle all the way,

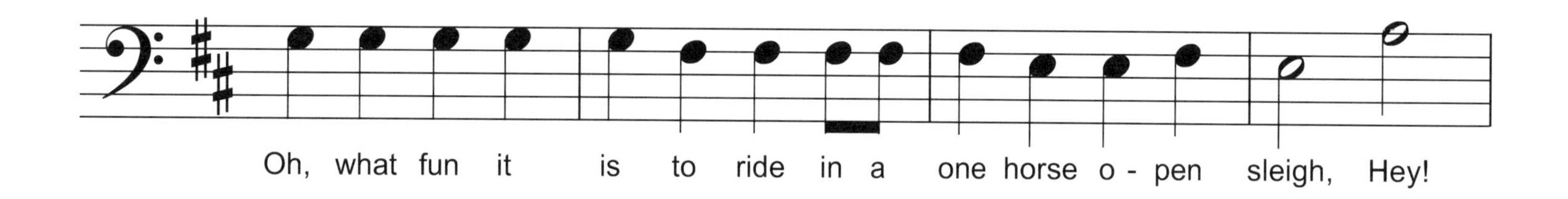
Oh, what fun it is to ride in a one horse o - pen sleigh, Hey!

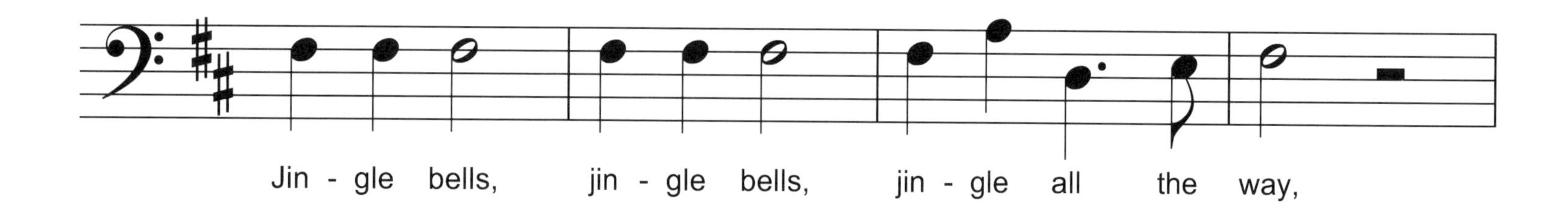
Jin - gle bells, jin - gle bells, jin - gle all the way,

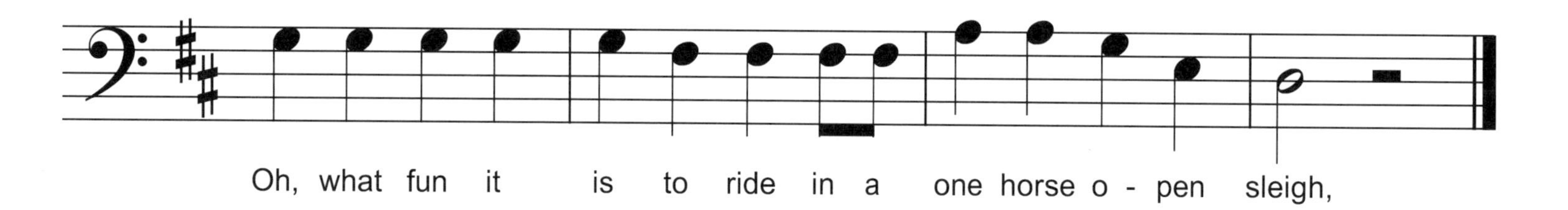
Oh, what fun it is to ride in a one horse o - pen sleigh,

9-10-17

Merry dance

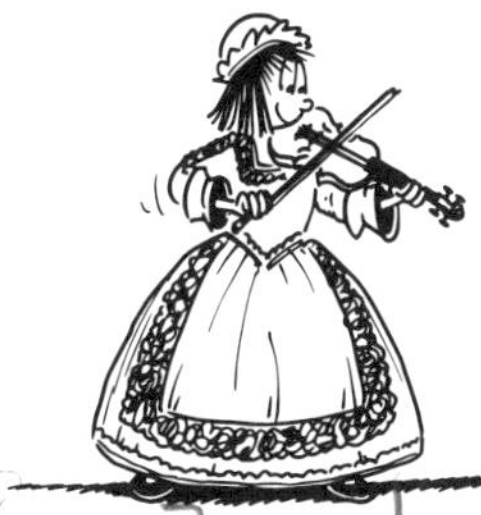

16C French melody

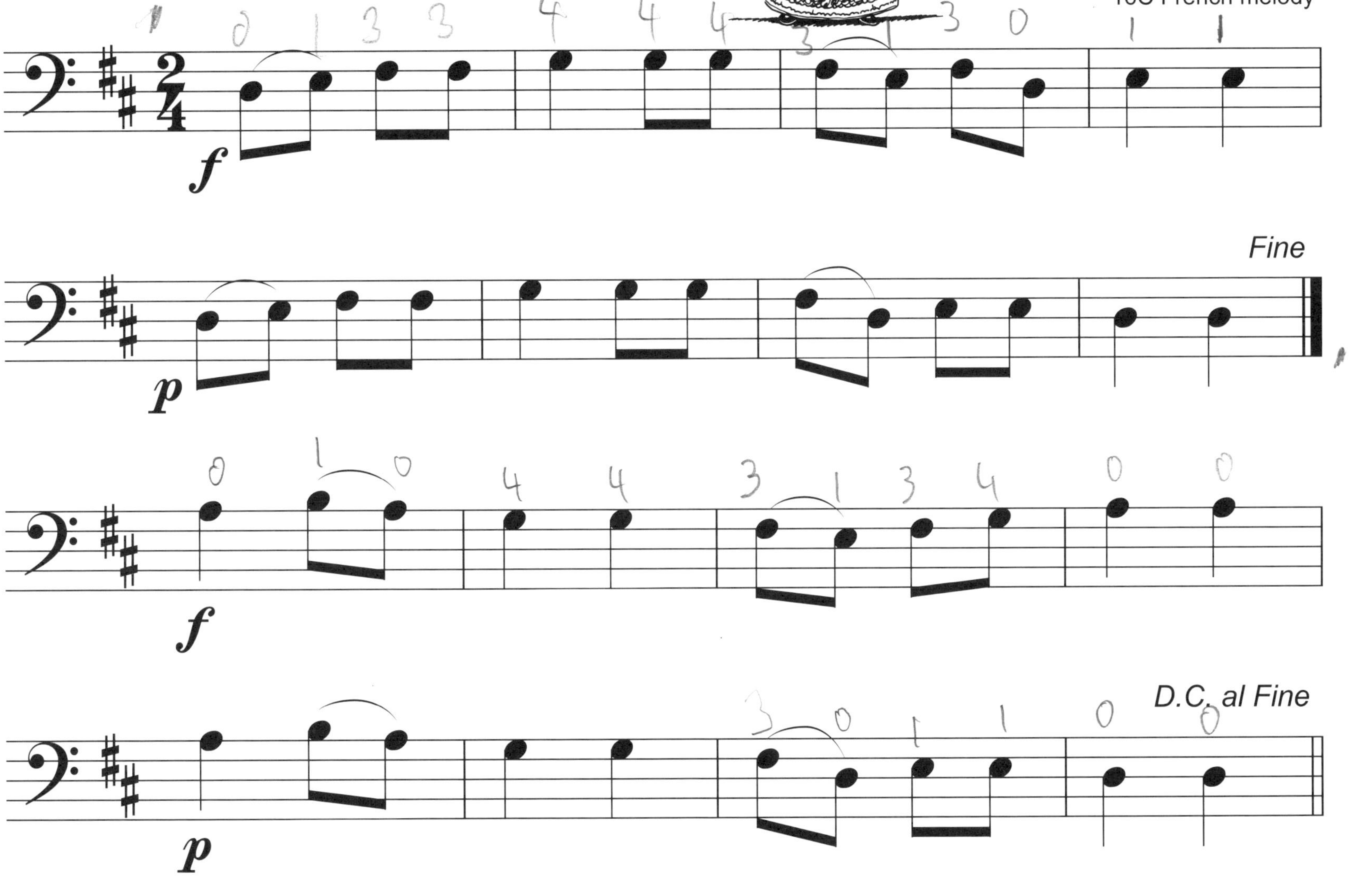
f
Fine
p
f
D.C. al Fine
p

Bend backs

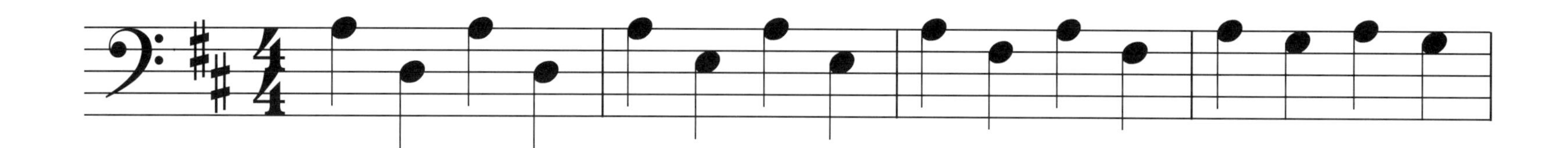

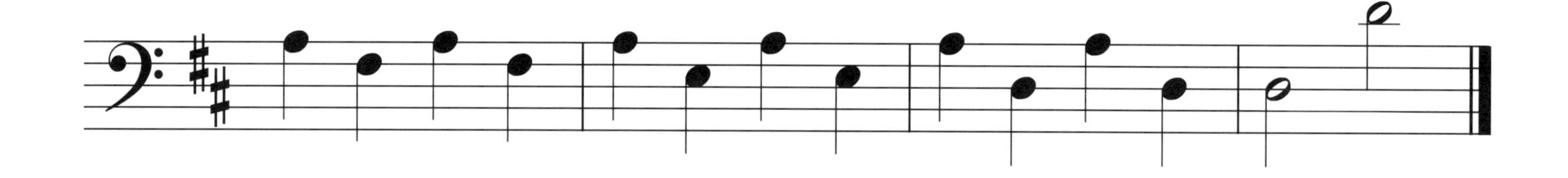

Rock-a-bye baby

Trad.

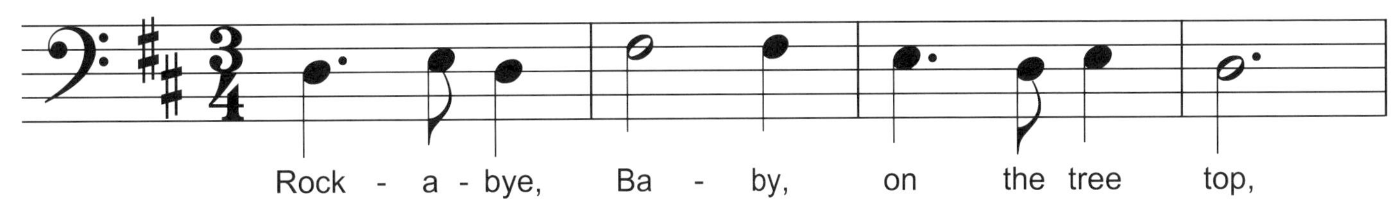
Rock - a - bye, Ba - by, on the tree top,

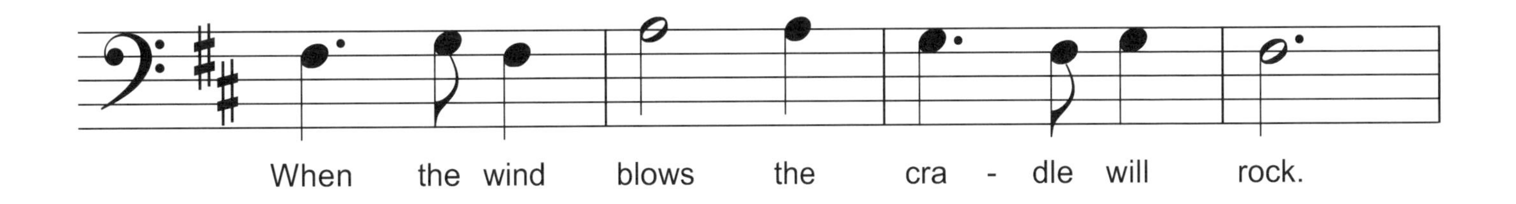
When the wind blows the cra - dle will rock.

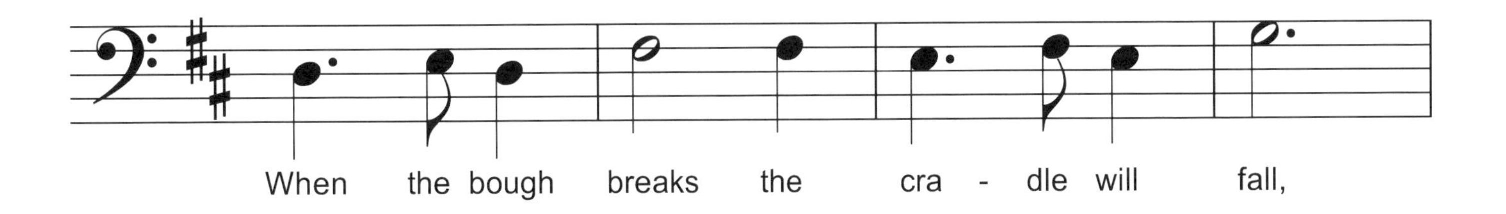
When the bough breaks the cra - dle will fall,

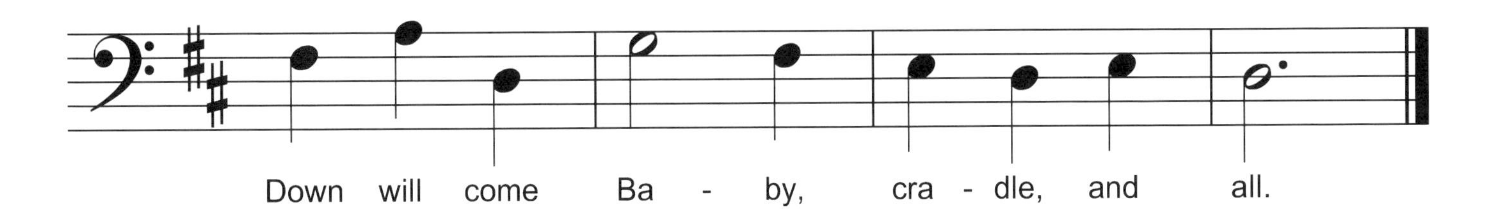
Down will come Ba - by, cra - dle, and all.

Au clair de la lune

French
Fine
Au clair de la lu - ne, mon a - mi Pier - rot,
Ouv - re moi ta por - te, pour l'a - mour de Dieu.
Je n'ai pas de plu - me, pour é - crire un mot,
D.C. al Fine
Ma chan-delle est mor - te, Je n'ai plus de feu;

Round

A. Caldara
(1670-1736)

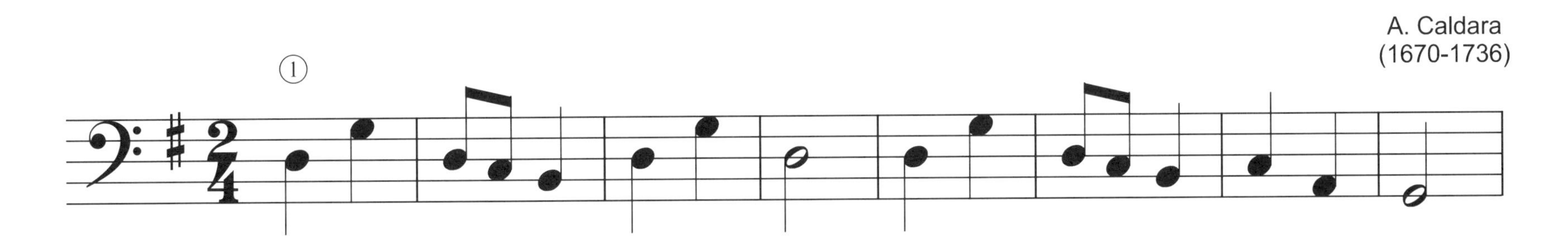
①

②

Canon

Hungarian folk song

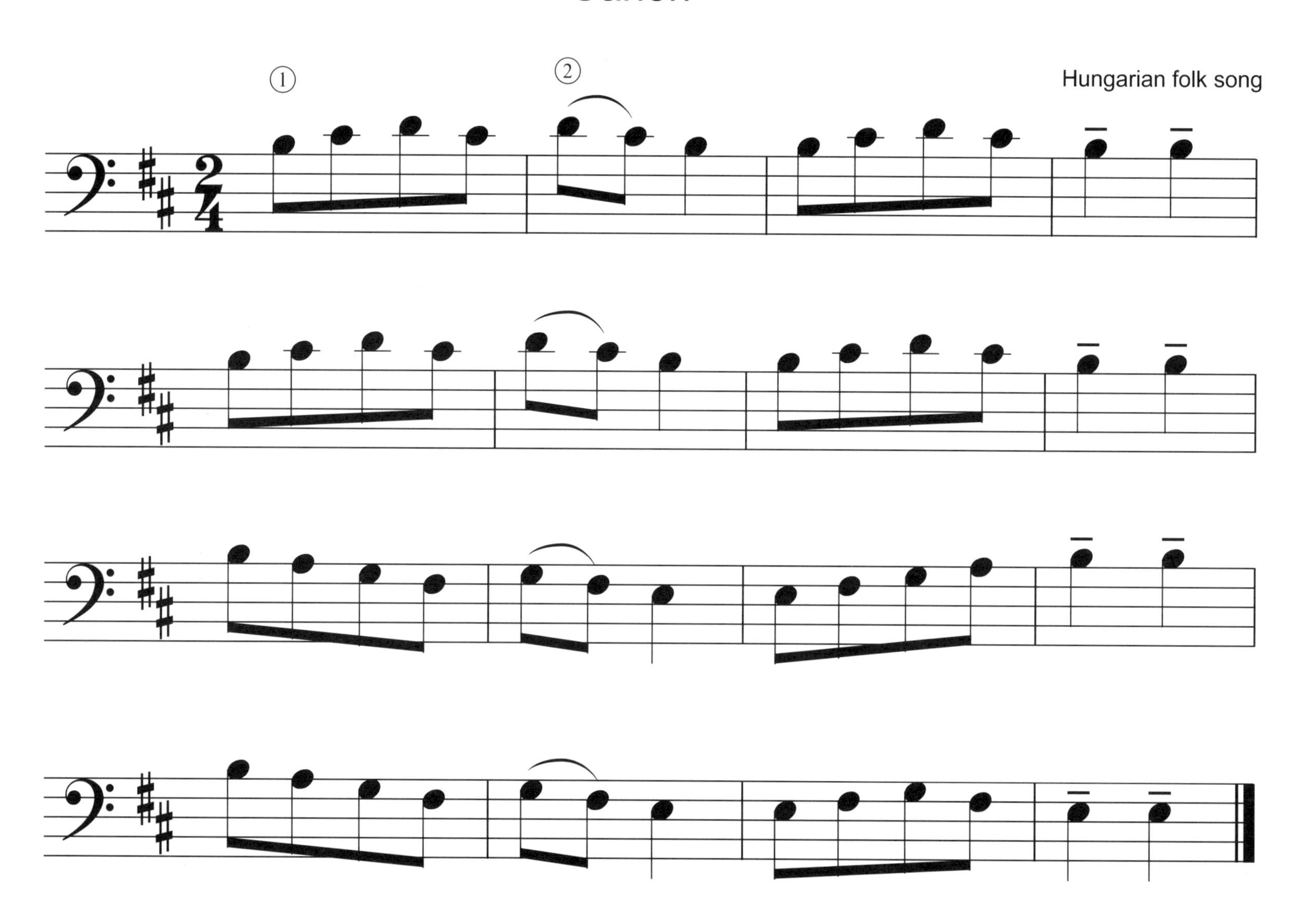
① ②

= ***tenuto*** = play full value

Barcarolle

J. Offenbach

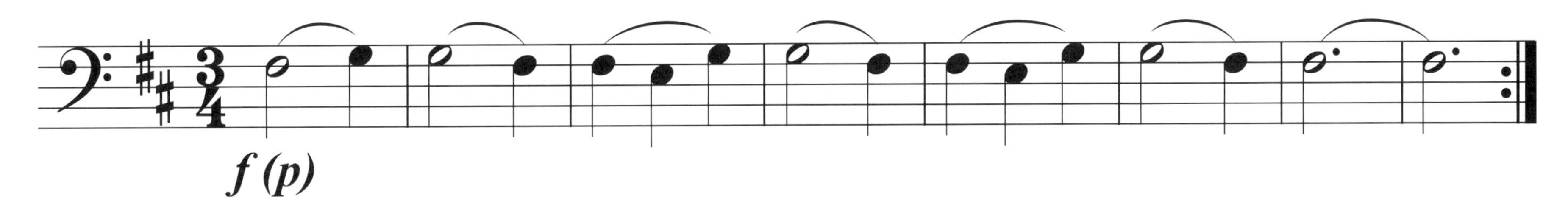
f (p)

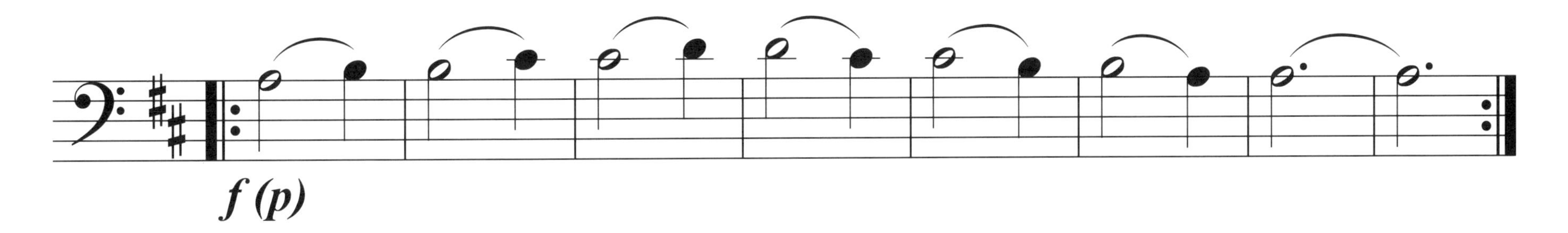
f (p)

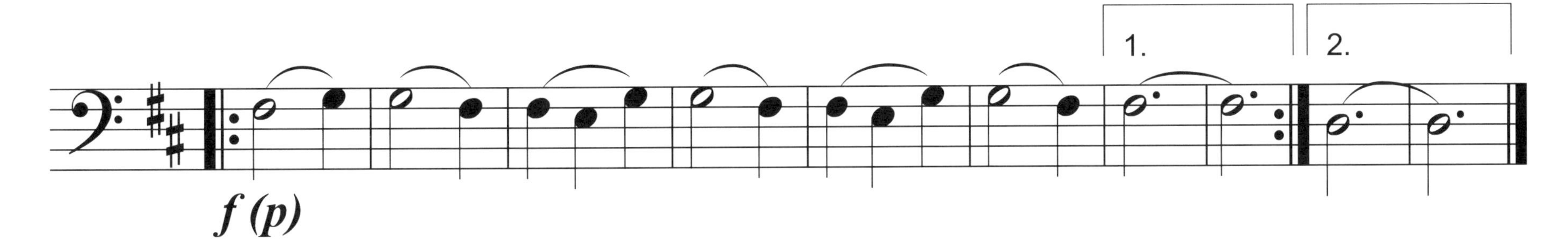
1.
2.
f (p)

Donkey riding

Trad.

Were you ev - er in Que - bec, Stow - ing tim - ber on the deck,

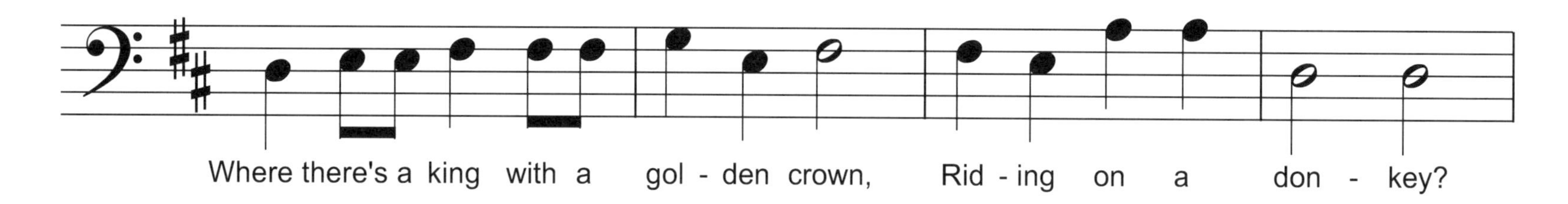
Where there's a king with a gol - den crown, Rid - ing on a don - key?

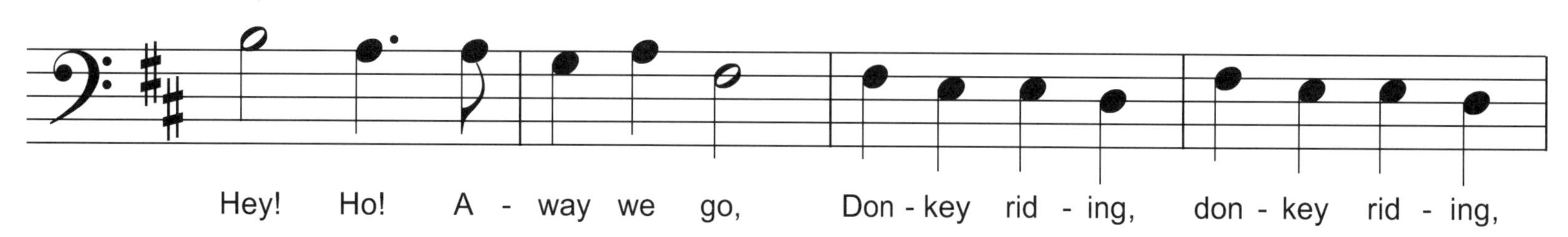
Hey! Ho! A - way we go, Don - key rid - ing, don - key rid - ing,

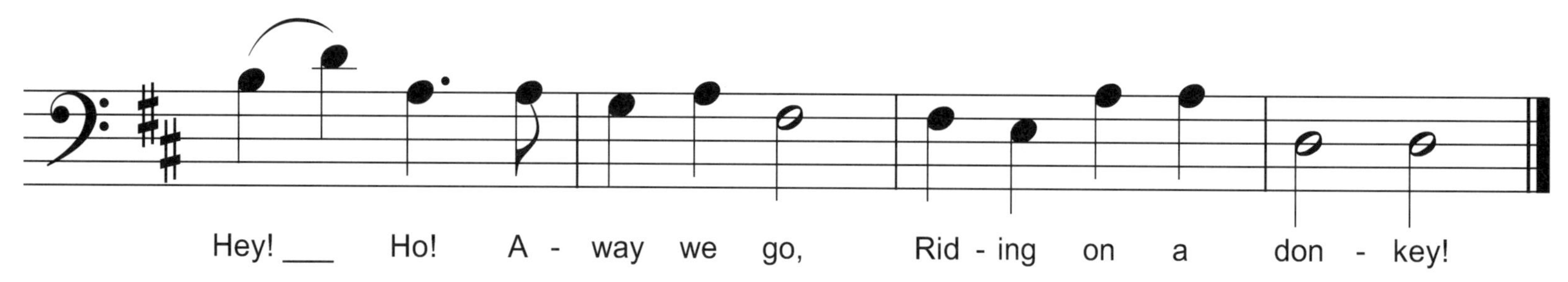
Hey! ___ Ho! A - way we go, Rid - ing on a don - key!

Winds through the olive trees

Trad. French

Winds through the o - live trees soft - ly did blow, a -

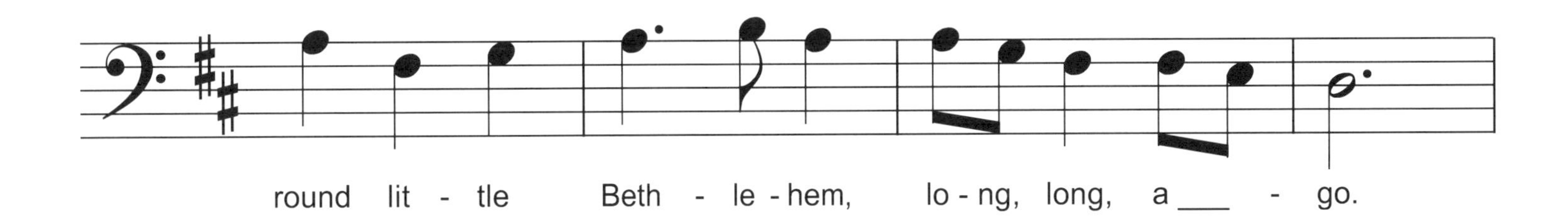
round lit - tle Beth - le - hem, lo - ng, long, a ___ - go.

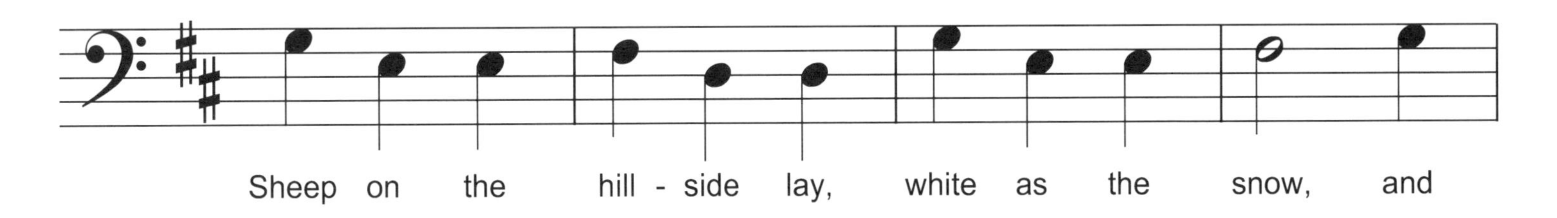
Sheep on the hill - side lay, white as the snow, and

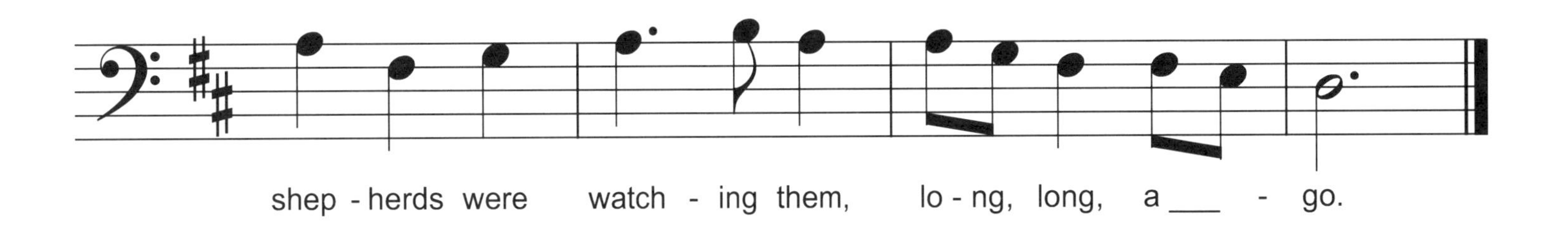
shep - herds were watch - ing them, lo - ng, long, a ___ - go.

See-saw

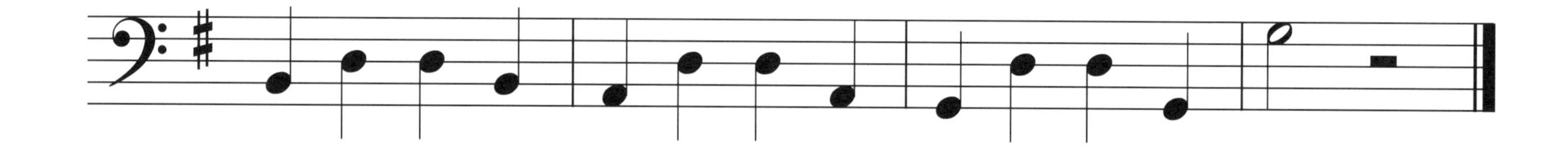

Can-can

J. Offenbach

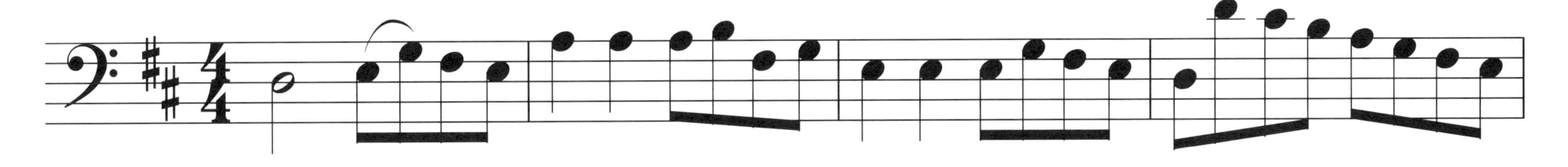

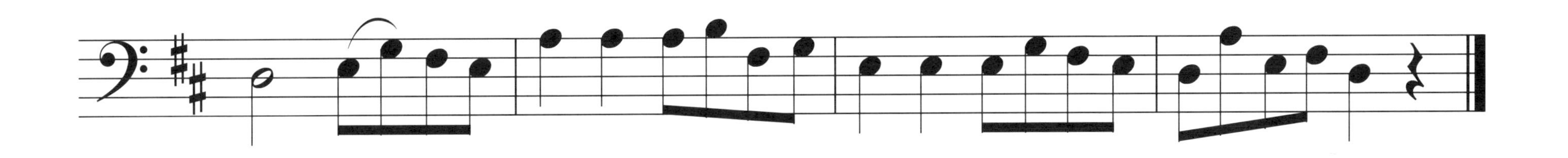

Leap frog

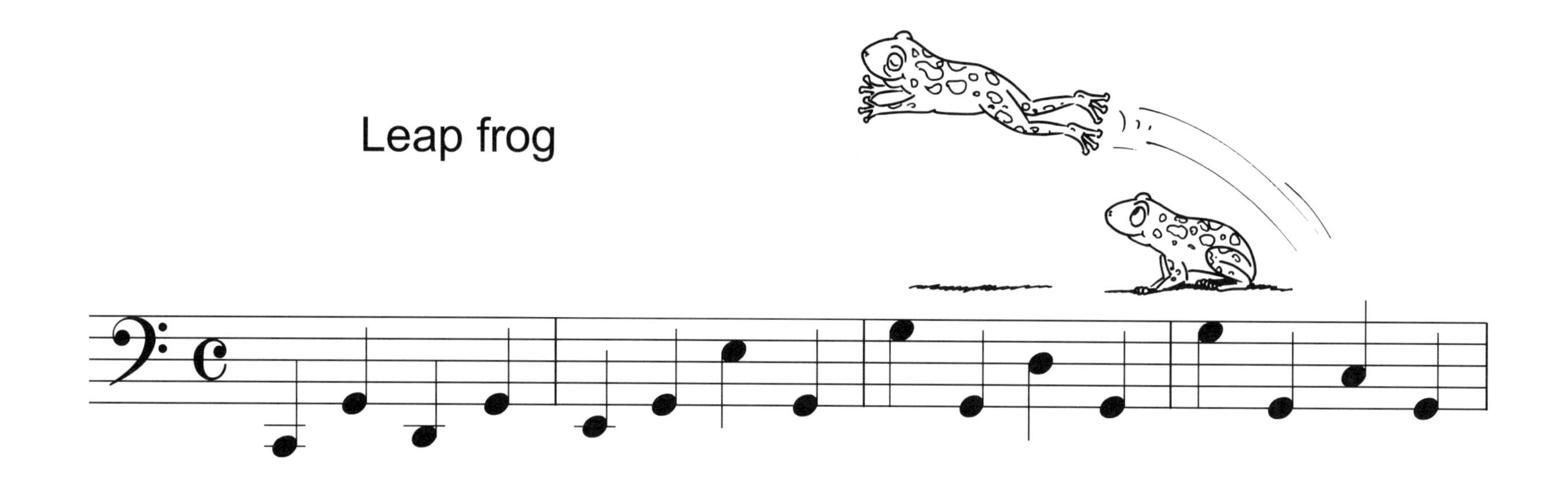

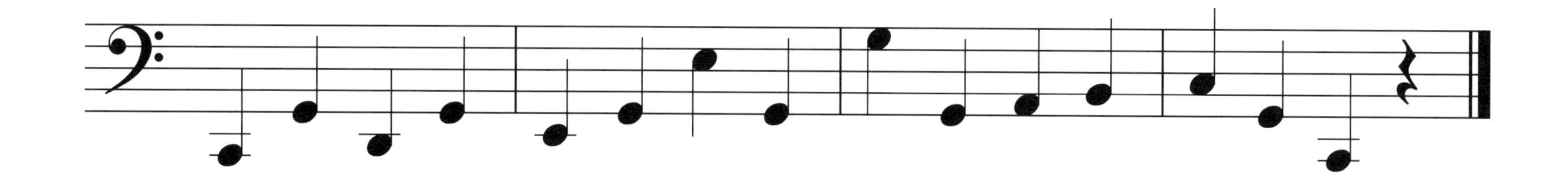

Floating clouds

mf legato
cresc.
f
dim.
p
rit.

D major scale and arpeggio

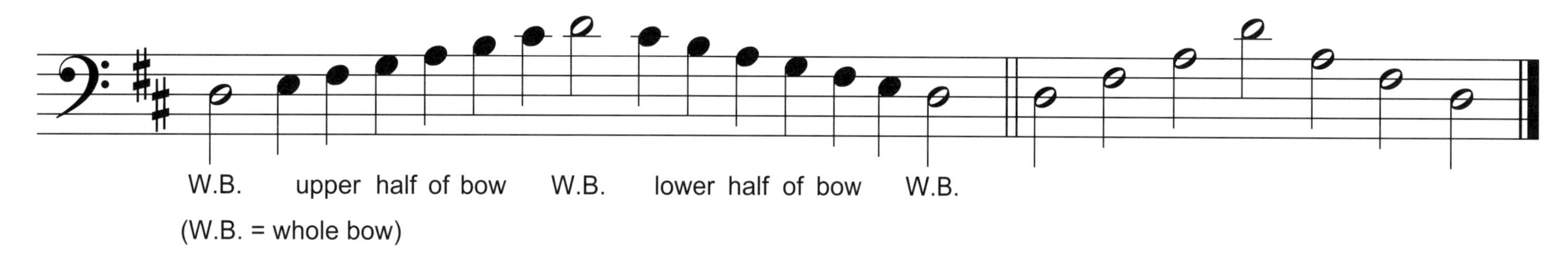
W.B.
upper half of bow
W.B.
lower half of bow
W.B.
(W.B. = whole bow)

G major scale and arpeggio

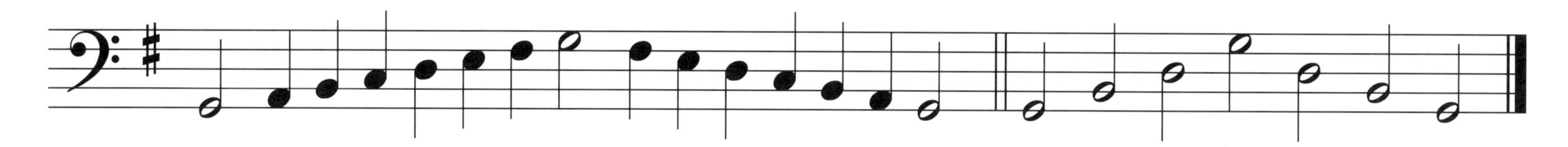

C major scale and arpeggio

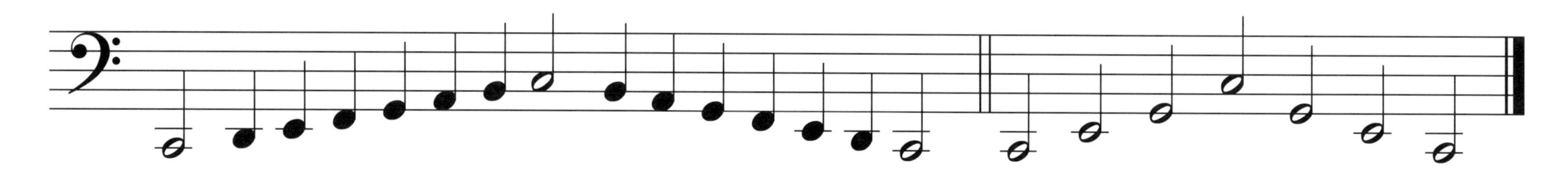

Bowing variations (scale, arpeggio or melody)

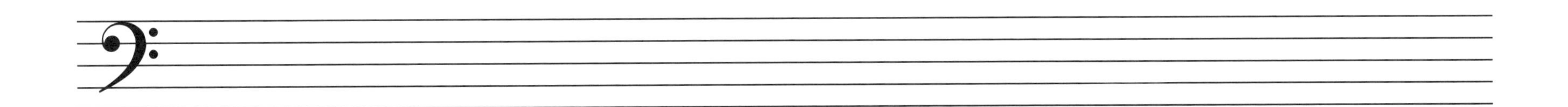

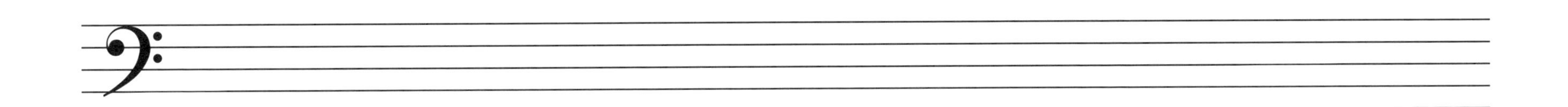

① 

②

③

④

⑤ 

⑥

⑦

⑧

Name these signs and terms.

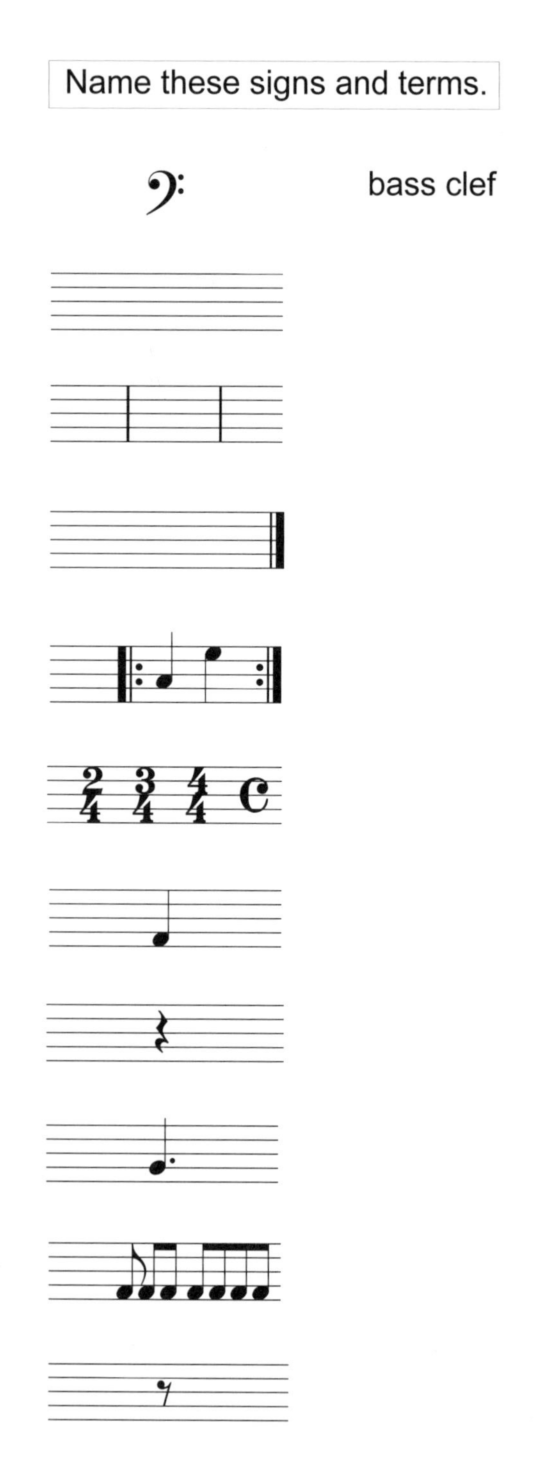

bass clef

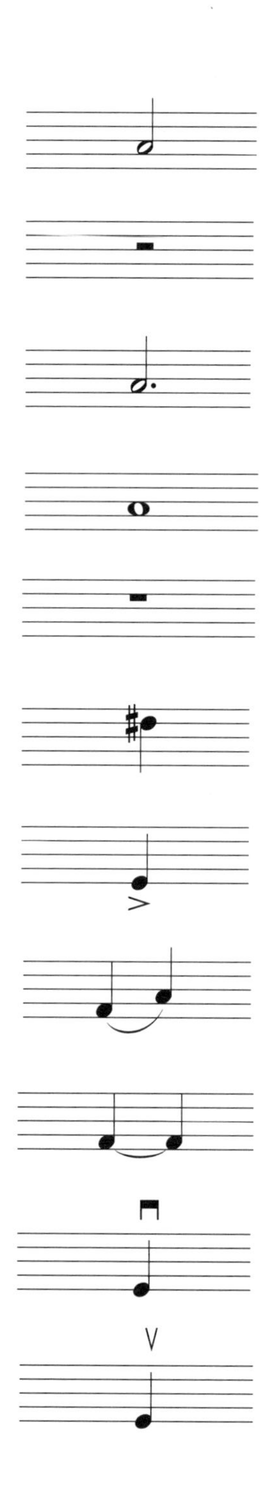

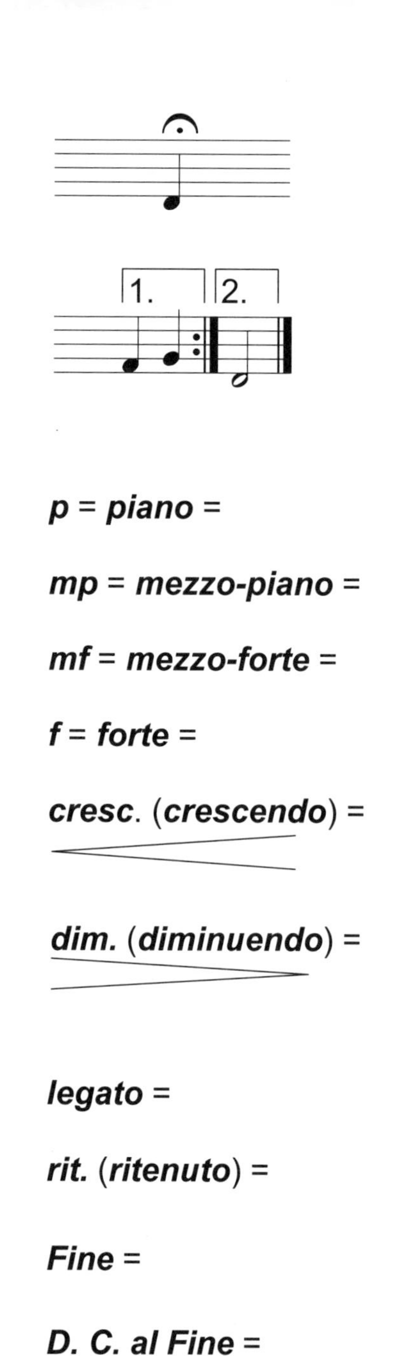

1.
2.

***p* = *piano* =**

***mp* = *mezzo-piano* =**

***mf* = *mezzo-forte* =**

***f* = *forte* =**

***cresc.* (*crescendo*) =**

***dim.* (*diminuendo*) =**

***legato* =**

***rit.* (*ritenuto*) =**

***Fine* =**

***D. C. al Fine* =**